THE

CPC

CPC

VISUALLY
Internalize the Standards

The Code of Professional Conduct
for Sign Language Interpreters

Provided by

DEAF DOORWAY

Published by

The CPC Visually - Internalize the Standards

ISBN 978-0-9994576-0-3

Deaf Doorway
PO Box 111
Fairview, TN 37062-0111

Books are available at CPCVisually.com

Published by:
Henry Lyon Books
789 State Route 94 E
Fulton, KY 42041

RID CPC used by permission of the Registry of Interpreters for the Deaf

Concept by Grayce F Fleet

Illustrations by Eric C Fleet

Cover Design by Faithe Thomas

Special thanks to Deaf Go: Deaf Theological Center in Brentwood, TN for validating this visual method of study.

Printed in the USA

INTRODUCTION

Thank you for picking up this odd little book. It is proof you can think outside the box! We intentionally kept this book uncomplicated – no fancy computer graphics or lengthy explanations. We simply took apart the Code of Professional Conduct (CPC) and created straightforward drawings that you can duplicate easily on scrap paper. Deaf Doorway believes that Deaf people should have access to quality sign language interpreters who provide a trusted source of communication. By working with these drawings, you can internalize the standards presented in the CPC and gain confidence that you are providing that trusted source.

Deaf Doorway is composed of a team, Eric and Grayce Fleet, who have been married for over 25 years. Because Eric is Deaf, they have observed intimately the impact of seemingly trivial choices made by interpreters. Grayce has been an American Sign Language interpreter since 1989 and recognizes the importance of the CPC in the daily life of an interpreter. Together they tackled this project, eager to make it available to you.

We feel the CPC should be the guiding set of principles for sign language interpreters and should be intimately familiar to every sign language interpreter. Deaf Doorway has made it possible to make this resource available to you. We trust this book will provide you a different approach to the CPC, improve your interpreting skills, and in turn, as a quality interpreter, provide open doors to Deaf success!

How to Use

Each chapter in this workbook is divided into 7 sections, each designed specifically to improve recall of RID's Code of Professional Conduct.

The **Introduction** simply states the English version of each tenet of the CPC, the portion in bold is the portion covered by the chapter. The icon is also clearly illustrated.

The **Explanation** section provides comments defining elements of the icon.

Two **Imitation** icons are provided - Both icons are greyed in varying amounts, providing a place to practice by tracing all the elements.

The **Comprehension** section is divided into two parts. The first, *Expression*, is a chance to sketch the icon completely independently. The second is a chance for reflection. The *Reflection* portion provides an opportunity to make notes about the meaning of the tenet, or jot down questions for a mentor. As a reader, if your intention is to grasp a better understanding of the CPC and incorporate it in your daily life, the focus of your time should be spent on the *Comprehension* sections.

The purpose of the **Memorization** section is to ensure that all elements of the icon are firmly fixed in your memory. Feel free to copy these pages and practice as much as needed. If you are confident in your knowledge, then save some of the practice circles for future review.

The point of the *Acceleration* section is to get faster! Time yourself sketching the icon. If you would like to sketch all 45 icons in 10 minutes upon arrival for the certification exam, you should aim for 15 seconds for each one. Some are more simple and will take just a few seconds, but others will take longer, so plan accordingly.

Finally, each chapter ends with an **Orientation** exercise. Seeing the particular icon in context with all the icons you have learned for that tenet will reinforce their connection in your memory. As a reader, if your intention is to prepare for the certification exam and to quickly recall the CPC, the focus of your time should be spent on the *Acceleration* and *Orientation* sections.

At the end of the workbook section, you will find practice pages for the entire CPC. The opportunity to practice and time yourself will build confidence for when you are in the room for your certification exam. Again, try to complete the whole thing in 10 minutes or less.

Blessings as you embark on this journey and engraft the CPC Visually!

1.0 CONFIDENTIALITY

Tenet: Interpreters adhere to standards of confidential communication.

Illustrative Behavior - Interpreters:

1.1 Share assignment-related information only on a confidential and "as-needed" basis (e.g., supervisors, interpreter team members, members of the educational team, hiring entities).

1.2 Manage data, invoices, records, or other situational or consumer-specific information in a manner consistent with maintaining consumer confidentiality (e.g., shredding, locked files).

1.3 Inform consumers when federal or state mandates require disclosure of confidential information.

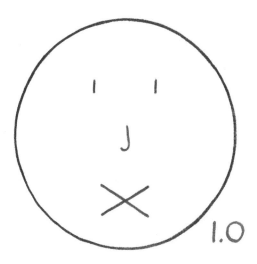

1.0 Tenet: Interpreters adhere to standards of confidential communication.

Explanation:

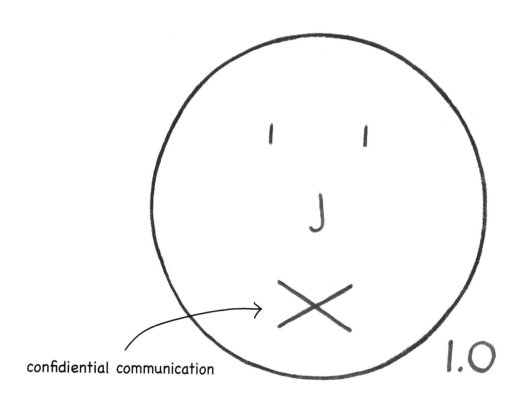

confidiential communication

Imitation: Trace the image below.

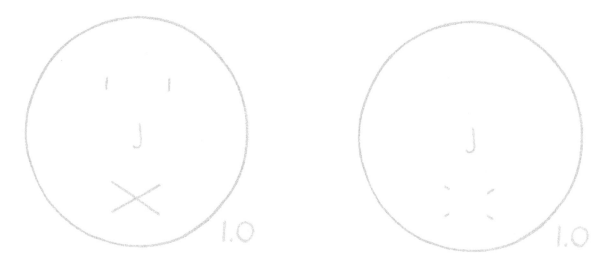

1.0

Comprehension:

Expression: Draw with understanding.

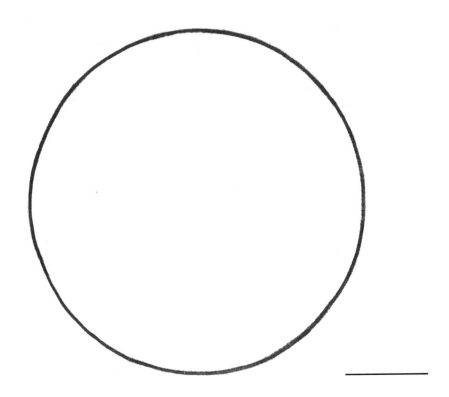

Reflection: Make notes about the meaning.

Clarify your understanding or write down questions to address with a mentor.

_____

_____

_____

_____

_____

Memorization: Practice drawing without turning back to see the original.

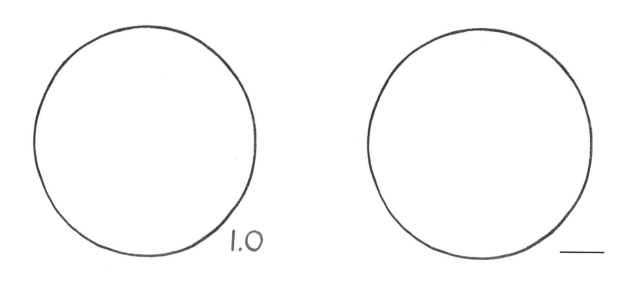

1.0

Check for accuracy. If you know it, save these others for future review.

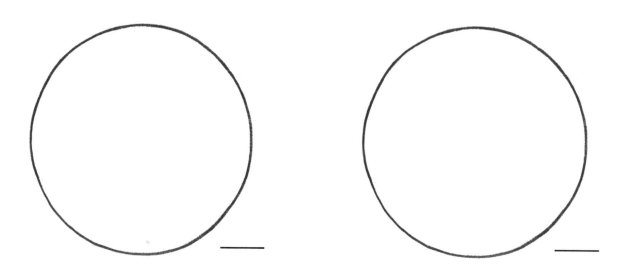

Acceleration: Practice drawing as quickly as possible.
Compare to original to ensure nothing was overlooked.

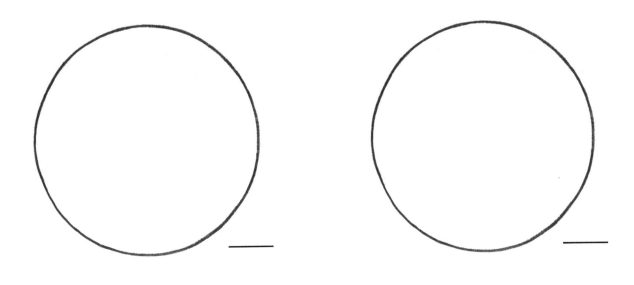

Time yourself. Be sure your drawing is complete within 15 seconds.
Jot down your time below. Be aware which drawings require more time.

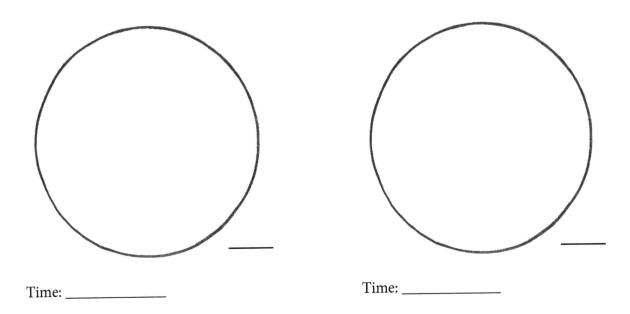

Time: _____

Time: _____

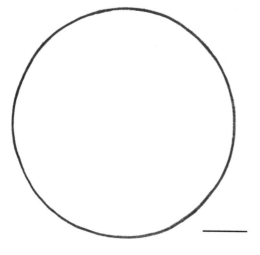

Orientation: Draw the icons you have learned in context. After your drawings are complete, express the meaning of each in sign language and then in spoken language.

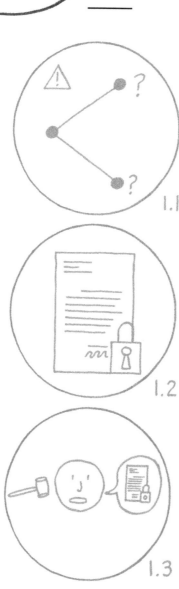

1.1

1.2

1.3

1.0 CONFIDENTIALITY

Tenet: Interpreters adhere to standards of confidential communication.

Illustrative Behavior - Interpreters:

1.1 **Share assignment-related information only on a confidential and "as-needed" basis (e.g., supervisors, interpreter team members, members of the educational team, hiring entities).**

1.2 Manage data, invoices, records, or other situational or consumer-specific information in a manner consistent with maintaining consumer confidentiality (e.g., shredding, locked files).

1.3 Inform consumers when federal or state mandates require disclosure of confidential information.

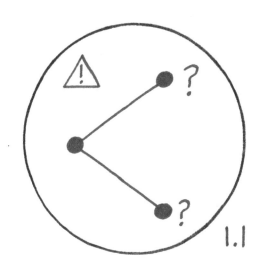

1.1

1.1 Share assignment-related information only
on a confidential and "as-needed" basis.

Explanation:

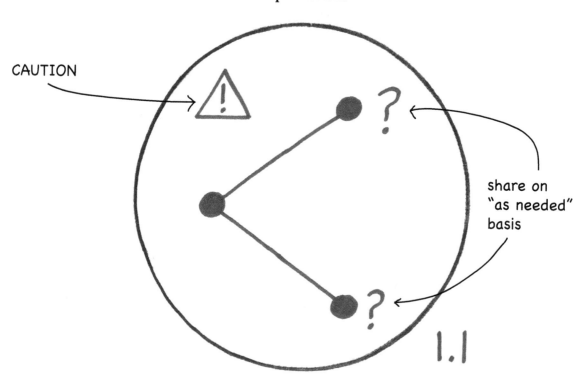

Imitation: Trace the image below.

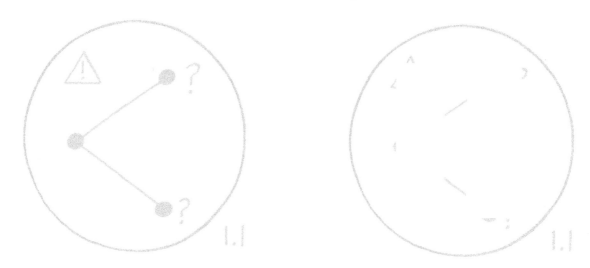

1.1

Comprehension:

Expression: Draw with understanding.

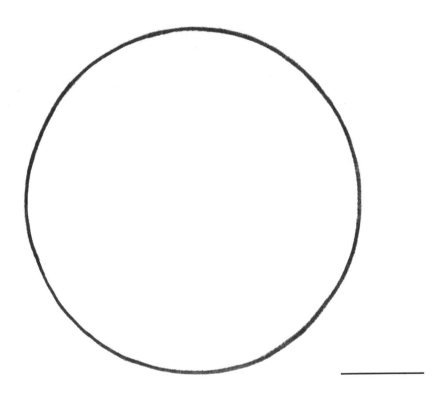

_____

Reflection: Make notes about the meaning.
Clarify your understanding or write down questions to address with a mentor.

_____

_____

_____

_____

_____

Memorization: Practice drawing without turning back to see the original.

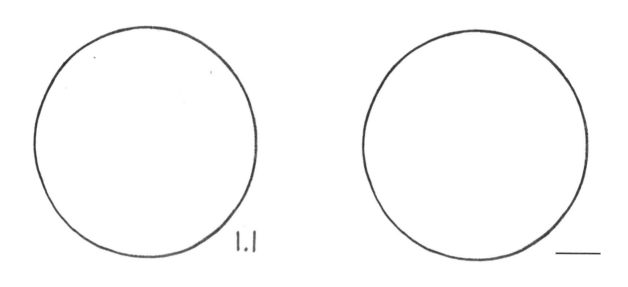

1.1

Check for accuracy. If you know it, save these others for future review.

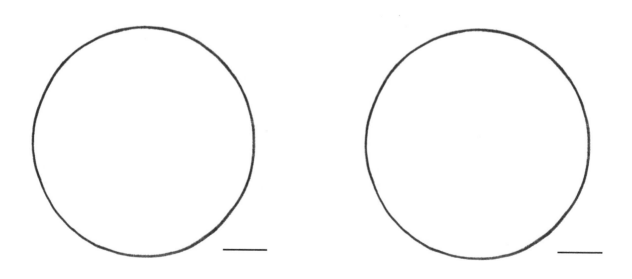

Acceleration: Practice drawing as quickly as possible.
Compare to original to ensure nothing was overlooked.

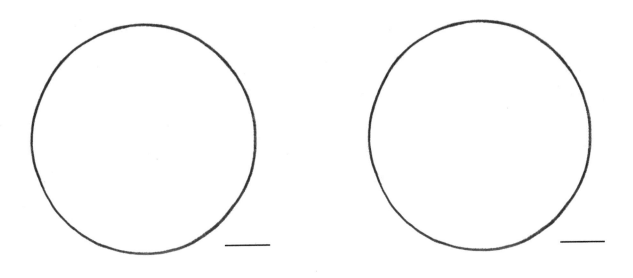

Time yourself. Be sure your drawing is complete within 15 seconds.
Jot down your time below. Be aware which drawings require more time.

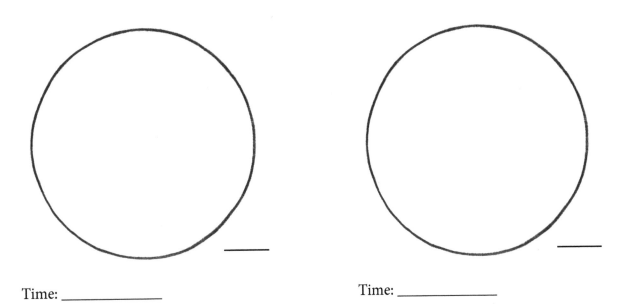

Time: _____   Time: _____

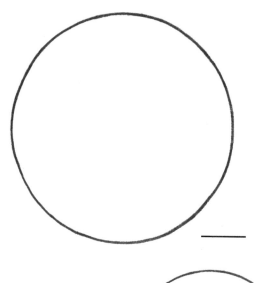

Orientation: Draw the icons you have learned in context. After your drawings are complete, express the meaning of each in sign language and then in spoken language.

___

___

1.2

1.3

1.0 CONFIDENTIALITY

Tenet: Interpreters adhere to standards of confidential communication.

Illustrative Behavior - Interpreters:

1.1 Share assignment-related information only on a confidential and "as-needed" basis (e.g., supervisors, interpreter team members, members of the educational team, hiring entities).

1.2 Manage data, invoices, records, or other situational or consumer-specific information in a manner consistent with maintaining consumer confidentiality (e.g., shredding, locked files).

1.3 Inform consumers when federal or state mandates require disclosure of confidential information.

1.2

1.2 Manage data, invoices, records, or other situational or consumer-specific information in a manner consistent with maintaining consumer confidentiality.

Explanation:

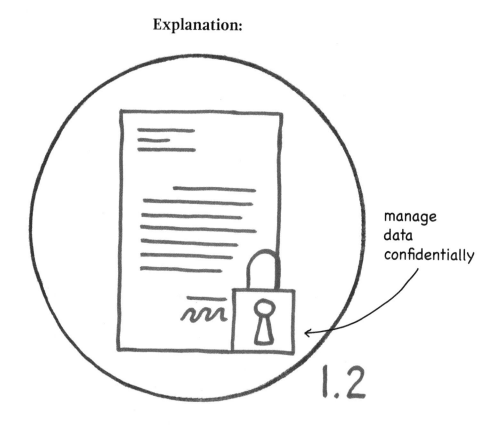

manage data confidentially

1.2

Imitation: Trace the image below.

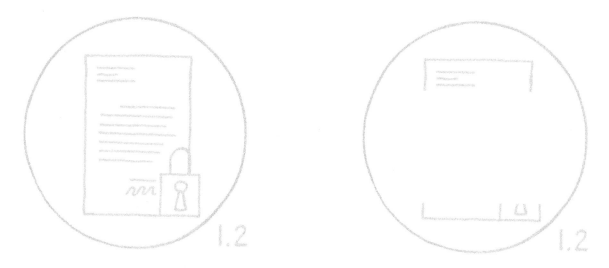

Comprehension:

Expression: Draw with understanding.

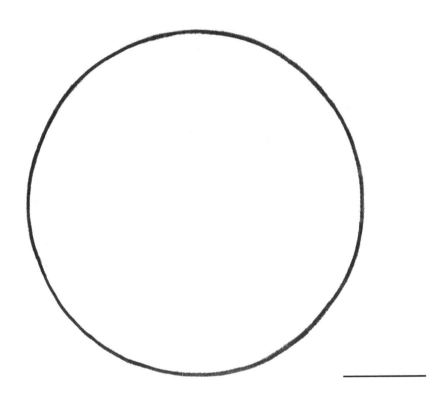

Reflection: Make notes about the meaning.
Clarify your understanding or write down questions to address with a mentor.

_____

_____

_____

_____

_____

Memorization: Practice drawing without turning back to see the original.

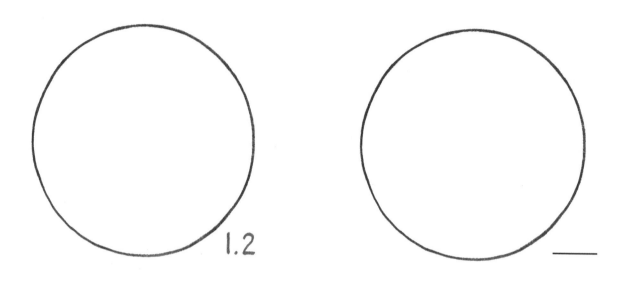

1.2

Check for accuracy. If you know it, save these others for future review.

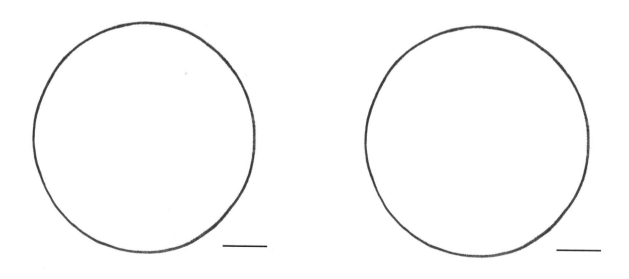

Acceleration: Practice drawing as quickly as possible.
Compare to original to ensure nothing was overlooked.

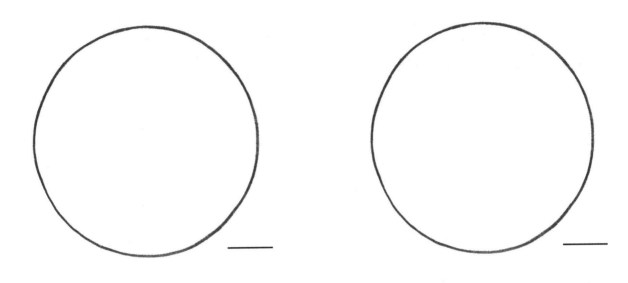

Time yourself. Be sure your drawing is complete within 15 seconds.
Jot down your time below. Be aware which drawings require more time.

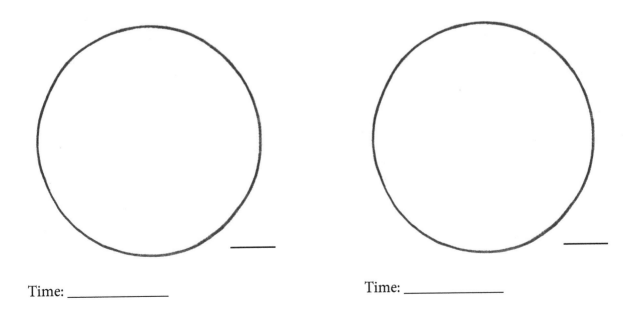

Time: _____   Time: _____

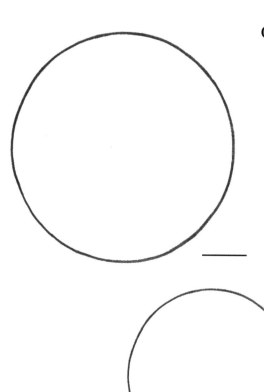

Orientation: Draw the icons you have learned in context. After your drawings are complete, express the meaning of each in sign language and then in spoken language.

___

___

___

1.3

1.0 CONFIDENTIALITY

Tenet: Interpreters adhere to standards of confidential communication.

Illustrative Behavior - Interpreters:

1.1 Share assignment-related information only on a confidential and "as-needed" basis (e.g., supervisors, interpreter team members, members of the educational team, hiring entities).

1.2 Manage data, invoices, records, or other situational or consumer-specific information in a manner consistent with maintaining consumer confidentiality (e.g., shredding, locked files).

1.3 Inform consumers when federal or state mandates require disclosure of confidential information.

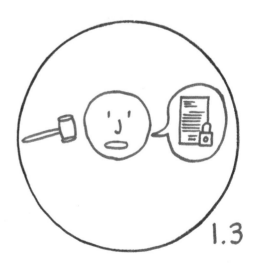

1.3

1.3 Inform consumers when federal or state mandates require disclosure of confidential information.

Explanation:

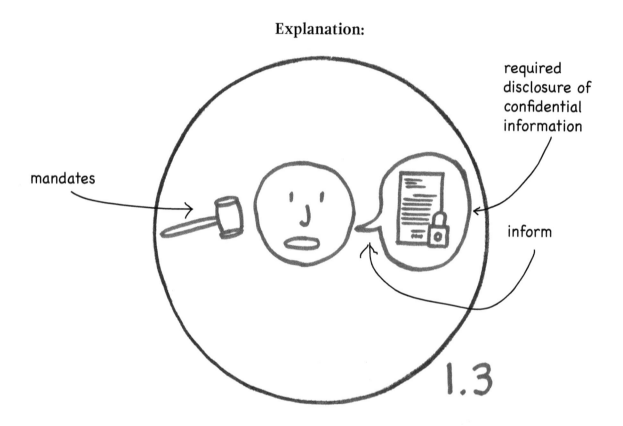

Imitation: Trace the image below.

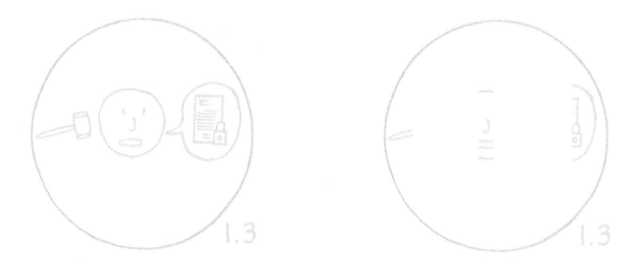

Comprehension:

Expression: Draw with understanding.

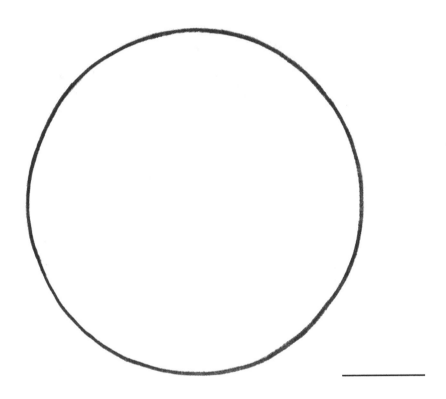

Reflection: Make notes about the meaning.
Clarify your understanding or write down questions to address with a mentor.

_____

_____

_____

_____

_____

Memorization: Practice drawing without turning back to see the original.

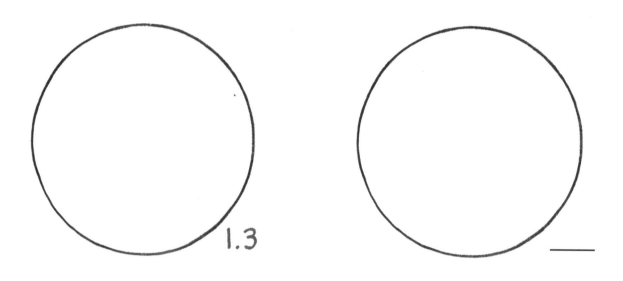

1.3

Check for accuracy. If you know it, save these others for future review.

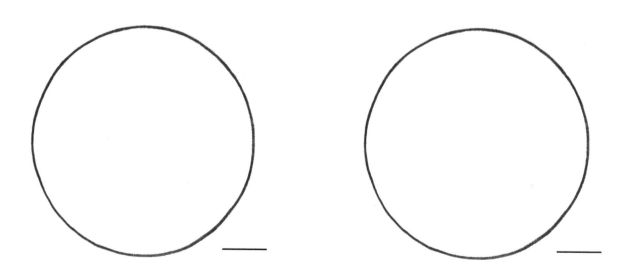

Acceleration: Practice drawing as quickly as possible.
Compare to original to ensure nothing was overlooked.

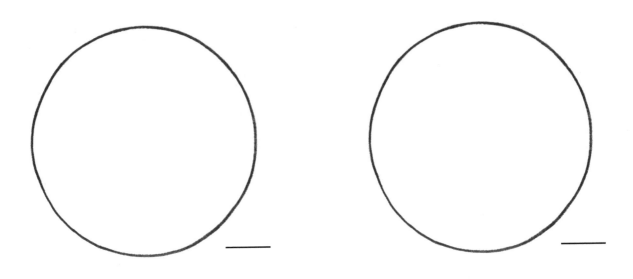

Time yourself. Be sure your drawing is complete within 15 seconds.
Jot down your time below. Be aware which drawings require more time.

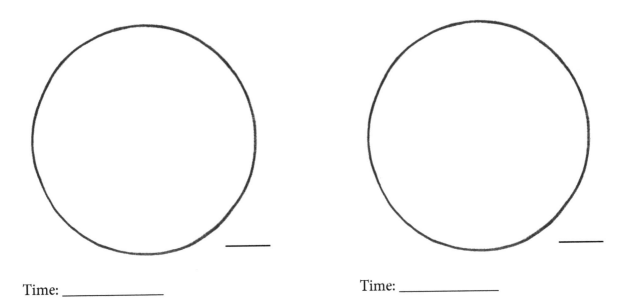

Time: _____

Time: _____

1.3

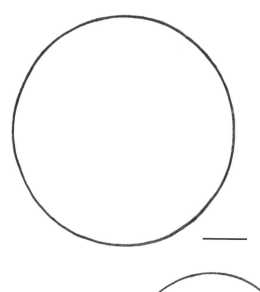

Orientation: Draw the icons you have learned in context. After your drawings are complete, express the meaning of each in sign language and then in spoken language.

___

___

___

___

1.3

2.0 PROFESSIONALISM

Tenet: Interpreters possess the professional skills and knowledge required for the specific interpreting situation.

Illustrative Behavior - Interpreters:

2.1 Provide service delivery regardless of race, color, national origin, gender, religion, age, disability, sexual orientation, or any other factor.

2.2 Assess consumer needs and the interpreting situation before and during the assignment and make adjustments as needed.

2.3 Render the message faithfully by conveying the content and spirit of what is being communicated, using language most readily understood by consumers, and correcting errors discreetly and expeditiously.

2.4 Request support (e.g., certified deaf interpreters, team members, language facilitators) when needed to fully convey the message or to address exceptional communication challenges (e.g. cognitive disabilities, foreign sign language, emerging language ability, or lack of formal instruction or language).

2.5 Refrain from providing counsel, advice, or personal opinions.

2.6 Judiciously provide information or referral regarding available interpreting or community resources without infringing upon consumers' rights.

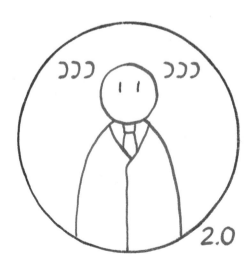

2.0 Tenet: Interpreters possess the professional skills and knowledge required for the specific interpreting situation.

Explanation:

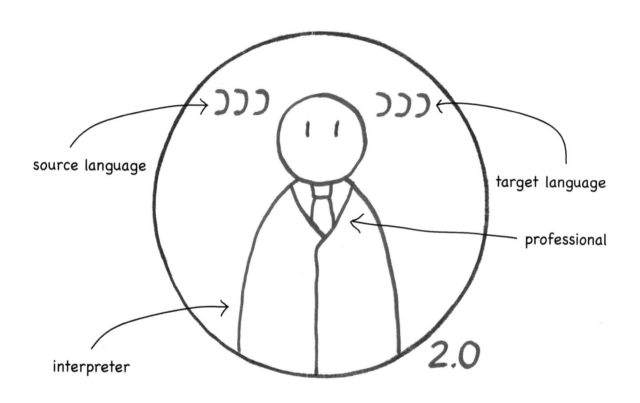

Imitation: Trace the image below.

Comprehension:

Expression: Draw with understanding.

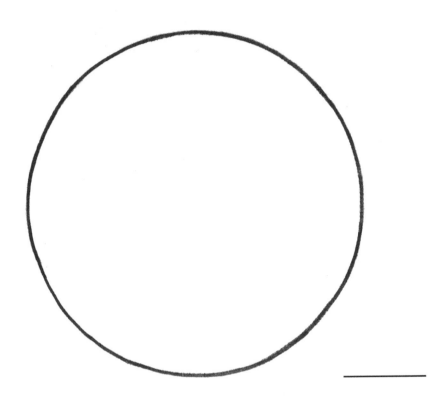

_____

Reflection: Make notes about the meaning.
Clarify your understanding or write down questions to address with a mentor.

_____

_____

_____

_____

_____

Memorization: Practice drawing without turning back to see the original.

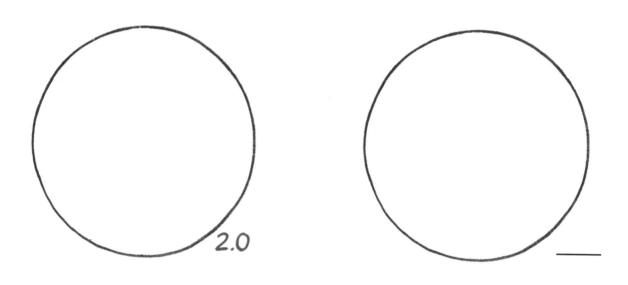

2.0

Check for accuracy. If you know it, save these others for future review.

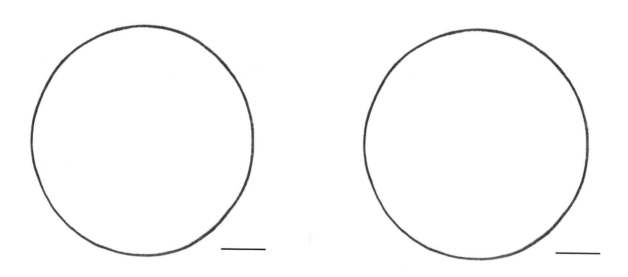

Acceleration: Practice drawing as quickly as possible.
Compare to original to ensure nothing was overlooked.

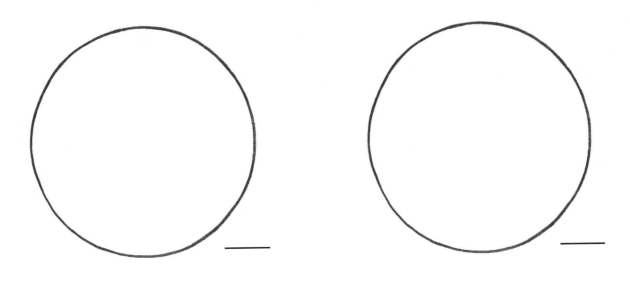

Time yourself. Be sure your drawing is complete within 15 seconds.
Jot down your time below. Be aware which drawings require more time.

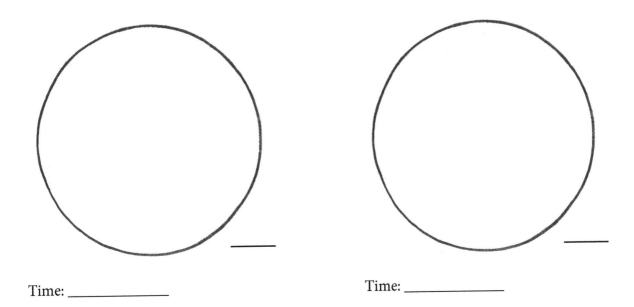

Time: _____

Time: _____

2.0

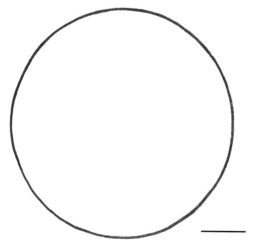

Orientation: Draw the icons you have learned in context. After your drawings are complete, express the meaning of each in sign language and then in spoken language.

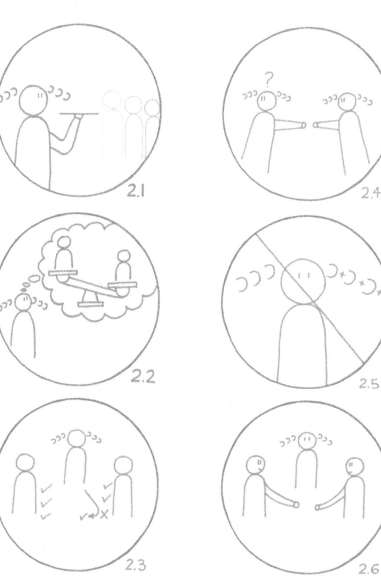

2.1

2.2

2.3

2.4

2.5

2.6

2.0 PROFESSIONALISM

Tenet: Interpreters possess the professional skills and knowledge required for the specific interpreting situation.

Illustrative Behavior - Interpreters:

2.1 **Provide service delivery regardless of race, color, national origin, gender, religion, age, disability, sexual orientation, or any other factor.**

2.2 Assess consumer needs and the interpreting situation before and during the assignment and make adjustments as needed.

2.3 Render the message faithfully by conveying the content and spirit of what is being communicated, using language most readily understood by consumers, and correcting errors discreetly and expeditiously.

2.4 Request support (e.g., certified deaf interpreters, team members, language facilitators) when needed to fully convey the message or to address exceptional communication challenges (e.g. cognitive disabilities, foreign sign language, emerging language ability, or lack of formal instruction or language).

2.5 Refrain from providing counsel, advice, or personal opinions.

2.6 Judiciously provide information or referral regarding available interpreting or community resources without infringing upon consumers' rights.

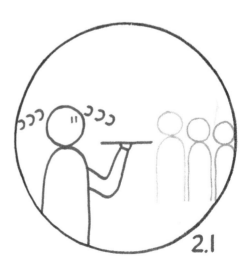

2.1

2.1 Provide service delivery regardless of race, color, national origin, gender, religion, age, disability, sexual orientation, or any other factor.

Explanation:

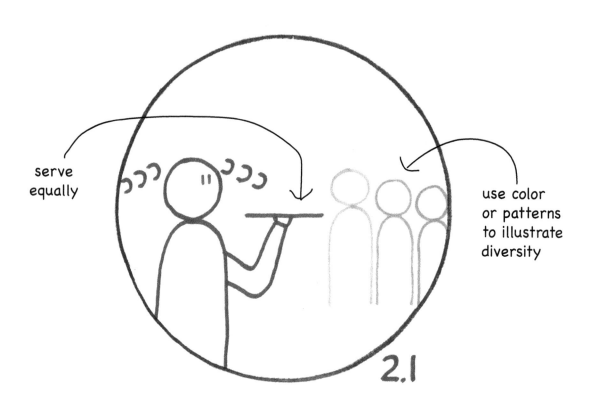

Imitation: Trace the image below.

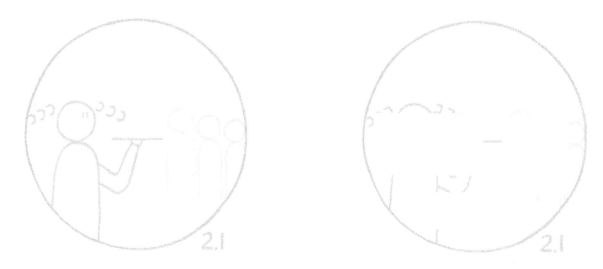

Comprehension:

Expression: Draw with understanding.

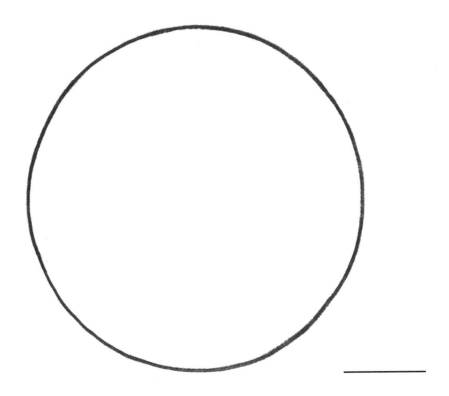

_____

Reflection: Make notes about the meaning.
Clarify your understanding or write down questions to address with a mentor.

_____

_____

_____

_____

Memorization: Practice drawing without turning back to see the original.

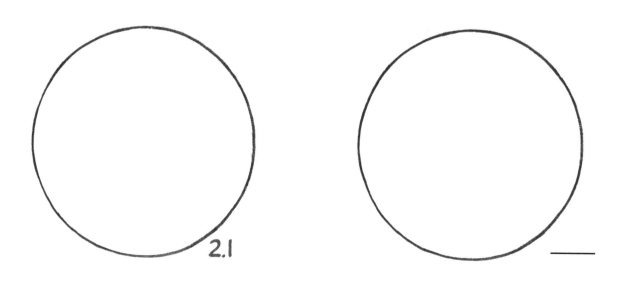

Check for accuracy. If you know it, save these others for future review.

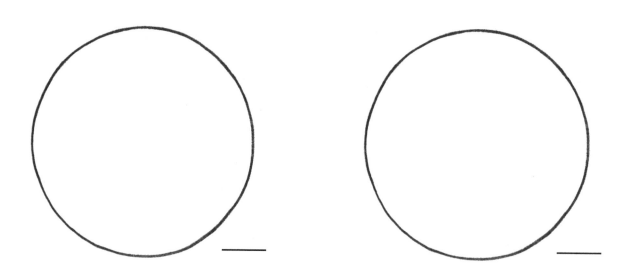

Acceleration: Practice drawing as quickly as possible.
Compare to original to ensure nothing was overlooked.

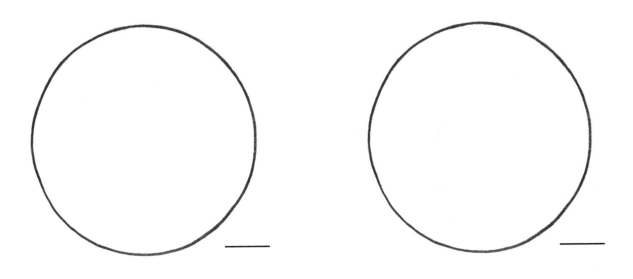

Time yourself. Be sure your drawing is complete within 15 seconds.
Jot down your time below. Be aware which drawings require more time.

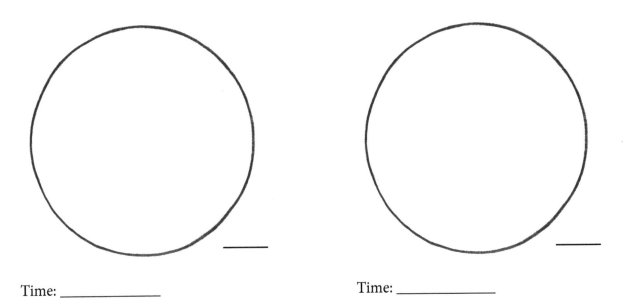

Time: _____   Time: _____

2.1

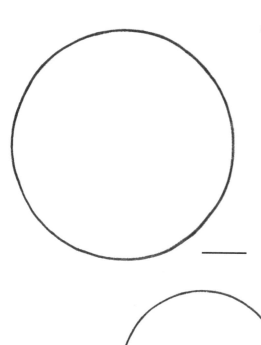

___

Orientation: Draw the icons you have learned in context. After your drawings are complete, express the meaning of each in sign language and then in spoken language.

___

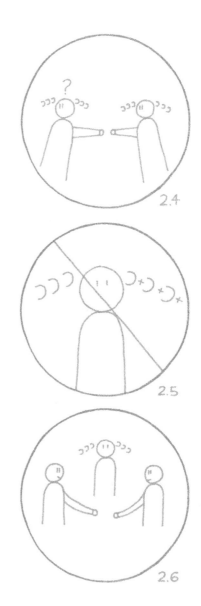

2.2

2.3

2.4

2.5

2.6

2.0 PROFESSIONALISM

Tenet: Interpreters possess the professional skills and knowledge required for the specific interpreting situation.

Illustrative Behavior - Interpreters:

2.1 Provide service delivery regardless of race, color, national origin, gender, religion, age, disability, sexual orientation, or any other factor.

2.2 Assess consumer needs and the interpreting situation before and during the assignment and make adjustments as needed.

2.3 Render the message faithfully by conveying the content and spirit of what is being communicated, using language most readily understood by consumers, and correcting errors discreetly and expeditiously.

2.4 Request support (e.g., certified deaf interpreters, team members, language facilitators) when needed to fully convey the message or to address exceptional communication challenges (e.g. cognitive disabilities, foreign sign language, emerging language ability, or lack of formal instruction or language).

2.5 Refrain from providing counsel, advice, or personal opinions.

2.6 Judiciously provide information or referral regarding available interpreting or community resources without infringing upon consumers' rights.

2.2

2.2 Assess consumer needs and the interpreting situation before and during the assignment and make adjustments as needed.

Explanation:

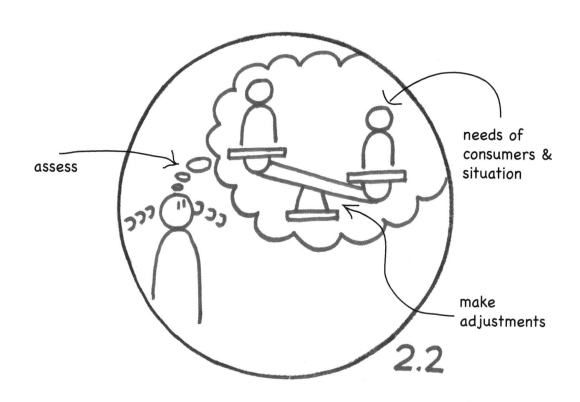

Imitation: Trace the image below.

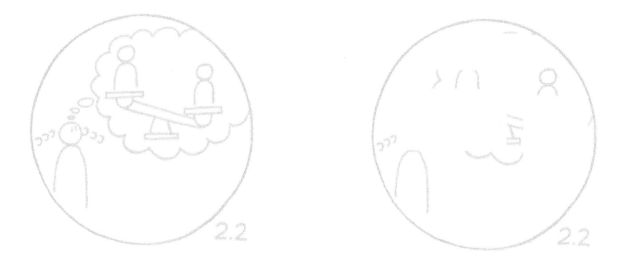

Comprehension:

Expression: Draw with understanding.

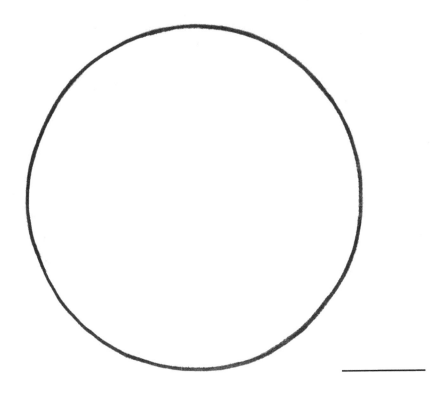

Reflection: Make notes about the meaning.
Clarify your understanding or write down questions to address with a mentor.

_____

_____

_____

_____

_____

Memorization: Practice drawing without turning back to see the original.

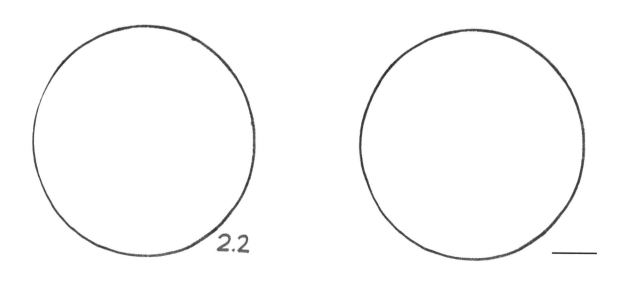

2.2

Check for accuracy. If you know it, save these others for future review.

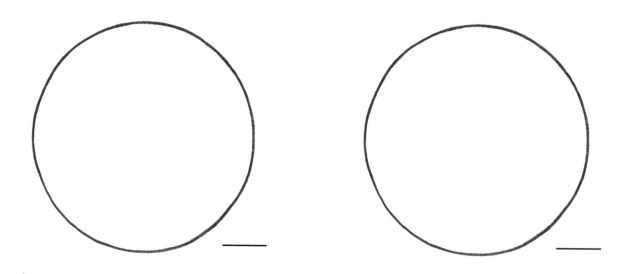

Acceleration: Practice drawing as quickly as possible.
Compare to original to ensure nothing was overlooked.

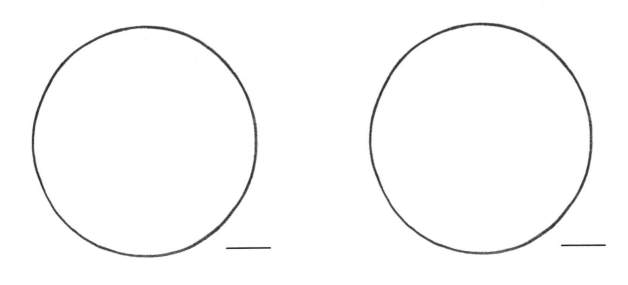

Time yourself. Be sure your drawing is complete within 15 seconds.
Jot down your time below. Be aware which drawings require more time.

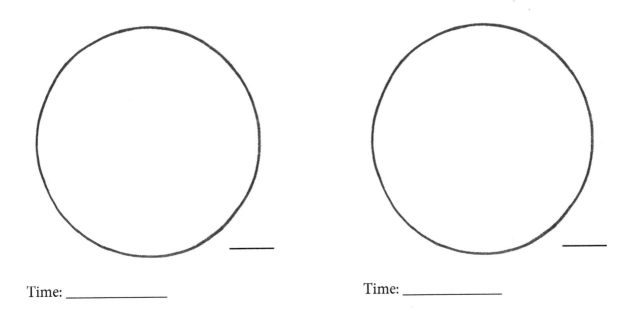

Time: _____   Time: _____

2.2

Orientation: Draw the icons you have learned in context. After your drawings are complete, express the meaning of each in sign language and then in spoken language.

2.4

2.5

2.3

2.6

2.2

2.0 PROFESSIONALISM

Tenet: Interpreters possess the professional skills and knowledge required for the specific interpreting situation.

Illustrative Behavior - Interpreters:

2.1 Provide service delivery regardless of race, color, national origin, gender, religion, age, disability, sexual orientation, or any other factor.

2.2 Assess consumer needs and the interpreting situation before and during the assignment and make adjustments as needed.

2.3 Render the message faithfully by conveying the content and spirit of what is being communicated, using language most readily understood by consumers, and correcting errors discreetly and expeditiously.

2.4 Request support (e.g., certified deaf interpreters, team members, language facilitators) when needed to fully convey the message or to address exceptional communication challenges (e.g. cognitive disabilities, foreign sign language, emerging language ability, or lack of formal instruction or language).

2.5 Refrain from providing counsel, advice, or personal opinions.

2.6 Judiciously provide information or referral regarding available interpreting or community resources without infringing upon consumers' rights.

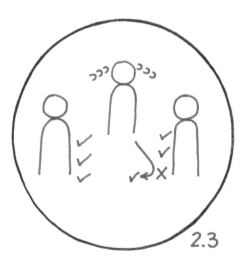

2.3

2.3 Render the message faithfully by conveying the content and spirit of what is being communicated, using language most readily understood by consumers, and correcting errors discreetly and expeditiously.

Explanation:

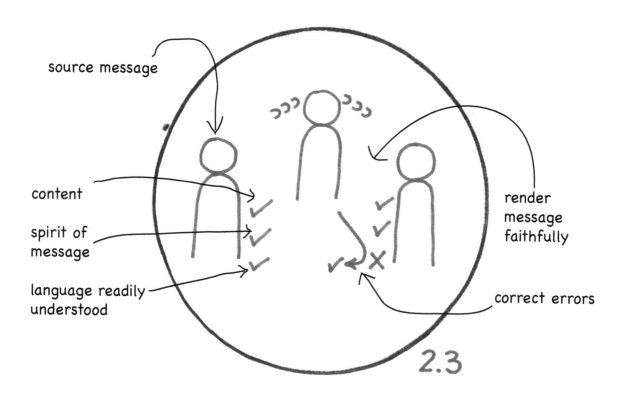

Imitation: Trace the image below.

2.3

Comprehension:

Expression: Draw with understanding.

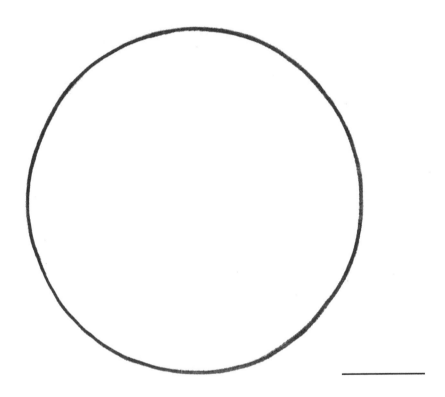

_____

Reflection: Make notes about the meaning.

Clarify your understanding or write down questions to address with a mentor.

_____

_____

_____

_____

_____

Memorization: Practice drawing without turning back to see the original.

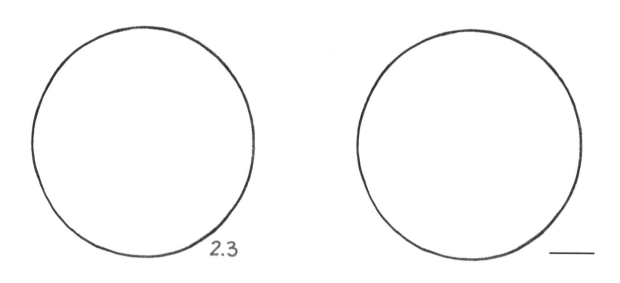

2.3

Check for accuracy. If you know it, save these others for future review.

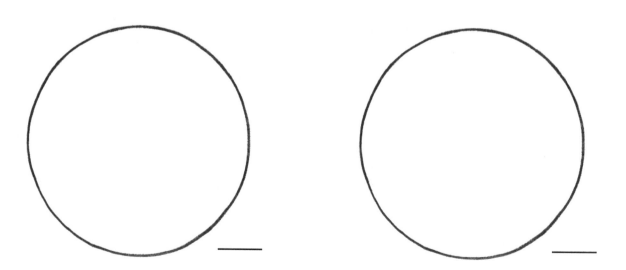

Acceleration: Practice drawing as quickly as possible.
Compare to original to ensure nothing was overlooked.

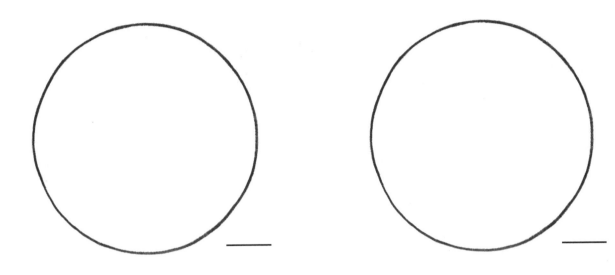

Time yourself. Be sure your drawing is complete within 15 seconds.
Jot down your time below. Be aware which drawings require more time.

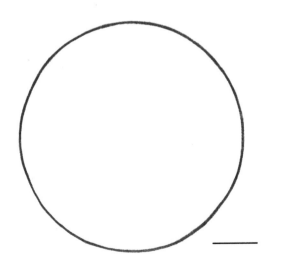

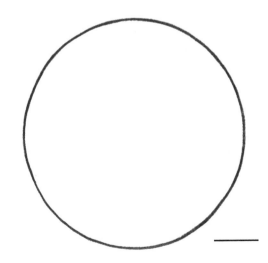

Time: _____

Time: _____

Orientation: Draw the icons you have learned in context. After your drawings are complete, express the meaning of each in sign language and then in spoken language.

2.4

2.5

2.6

2.3

2.0 PROFESSIONALISM

Tenet: Interpreters possess the professional skills and knowledge required for the specific interpreting situation.

Illustrative Behavior - Interpreters:

2.1 Provide service delivery regardless of race, color, national origin, gender, religion, age, disability, sexual orientation, or any other factor.

2.2 Assess consumer needs and the interpreting situation before and during the assignment and make adjustments as needed.

2.3 Render the message faithfully by conveying the content and spirit of what is being communicated, using language most readily understood by consumers, and correcting errors discreetly and expeditiously.

2.4 Request support (e.g., certified deaf interpreters, team members, language facilitators) when needed to fully convey the message or to address exceptional communication challenges (e.g. cognitive disabilities, foreign sign language, emerging language ability, or lack of formal instruction or language).

2.5 Refrain from providing counsel, advice, or personal opinions.

2.6 Judiciously provide information or referral regarding available interpreting or community resources without infringing upon consumers' rights.

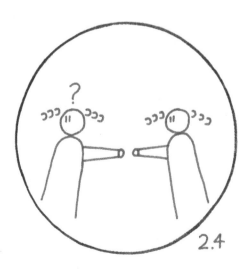

2.4

2.4 Request support when needed to fully convey the message or to address exceptional communication challenges.

Explanation:

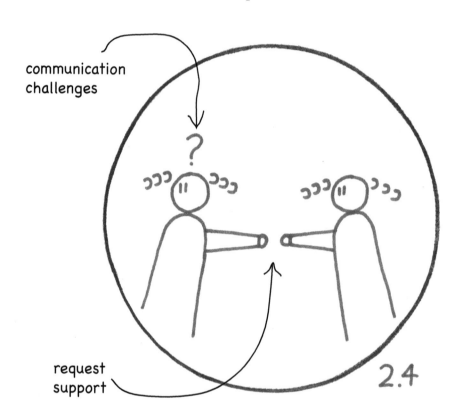

Imitation: Trace the image below.

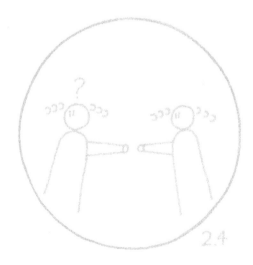

2.4

Comprehension:

Expression: Draw with understanding.

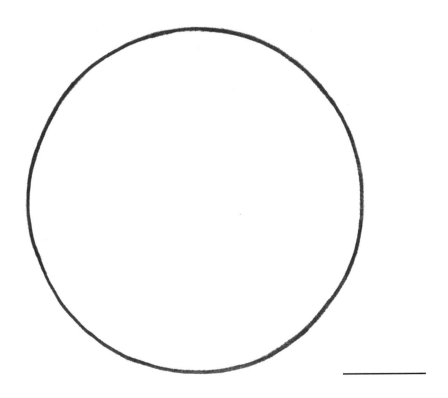

Reflection: Make notes about the meaning.
Clarify your understanding or write down questions to address with a mentor.

_____

_____

_____

_____

_____

Memorization: Practice drawing without turning back to see the original.

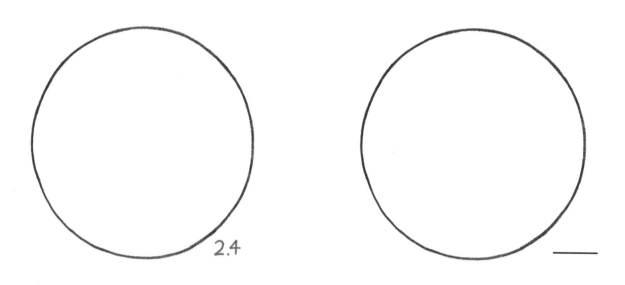

2.4

Check for accuracy. If you know it, save these others for future review.

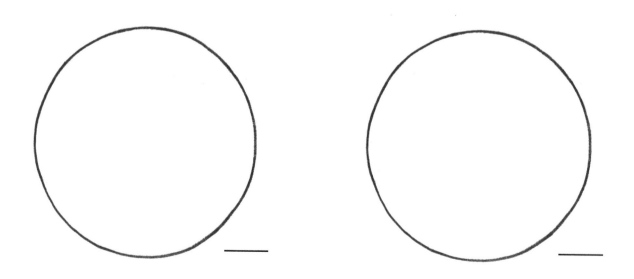

Acceleration: Practice drawing as quickly as possible.
Compare to original to ensure nothing was overlooked.

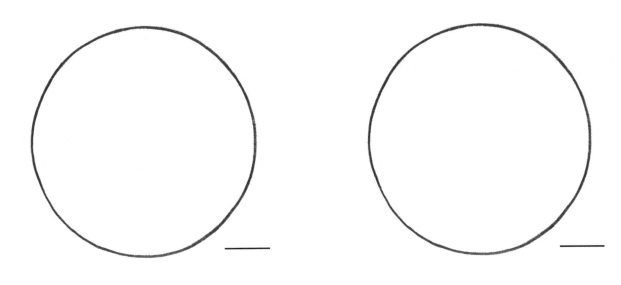

Time yourself. Be sure your drawing is complete within 15 seconds.
Jot down your time below. Be aware which drawings require more time.

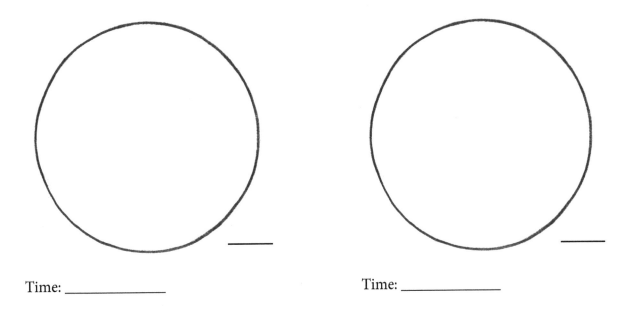

Time: _____   Time: _____

Orientation: Draw the icons you have learned in context. After your drawings are complete, express the meaning of each in sign language and then in spoken language.

2.5

2.6

2.4

2.0 PROFESSIONALISM

Tenet: Interpreters possess the professional skills and knowledge required for the specific interpreting situation.

Illustrative Behavior - Interpreters:

2.1 Provide service delivery regardless of race, color, national origin, gender, religion, age, disability, sexual orientation, or any other factor.

2.2 Assess consumer needs and the interpreting situation before and during the assignment and make adjustments as needed.

2.3 Render the message faithfully by conveying the content and spirit of what is being communicated, using language most readily understood by consumers, and correcting errors discreetly and expeditiously.

2.4 Request support (e.g., certified deaf interpreters, team members, language facilitators) when needed to fully convey the message or to address exceptional communication challenges (e.g. cognitive disabilities, foreign sign language, emerging language ability, or lack of formal instruction or language).

2.5 Refrain from providing counsel, advice, or personal opinions.

2.6 Judiciously provide information or referral regarding available interpreting or community resources without infringing upon consumers' rights.

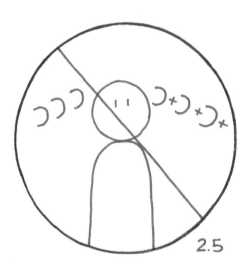

2.5

2.5 Refrain from providing counsel, advice, or personal opinions.

Explanation:

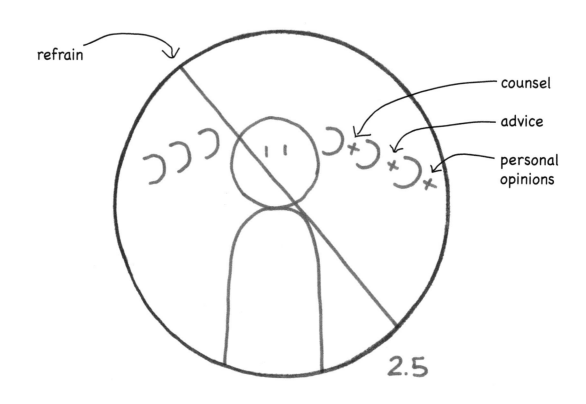

Imitation: Trace the image below.

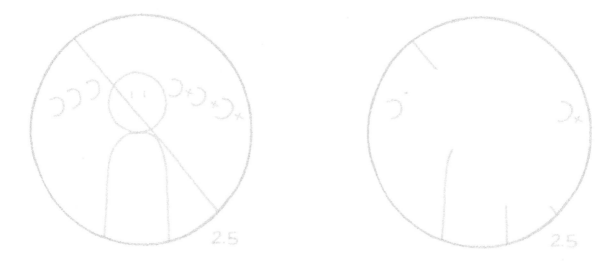

2.5

Comprehension:

Expression: Draw with understanding.

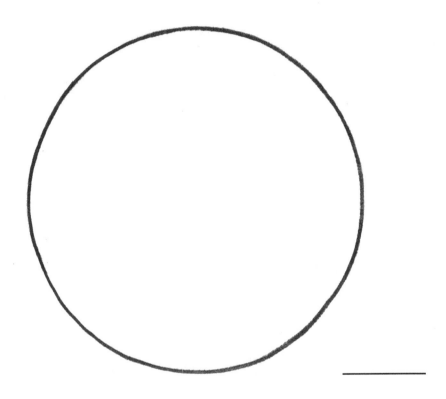

Reflection: Make notes about the meaning.
Clarify your understanding or write down questions to address with a mentor.

_____

_____

_____

_____

_____

Memorization: Practice drawing without turning back to see the original.

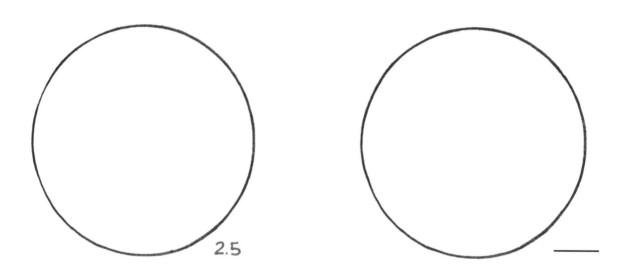

2.5

Check for accuracy. If you know it, save these others for future review.

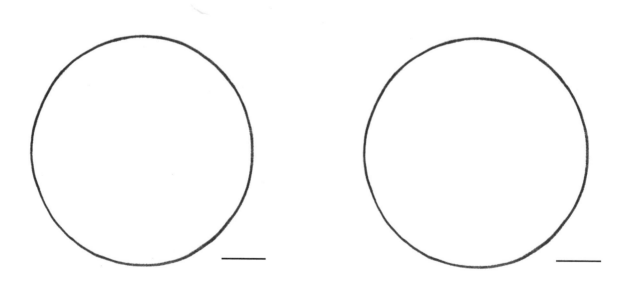

2.5

Acceleration: Practice drawing as quickly as possible.
Compare to original to ensure nothing was overlooked.

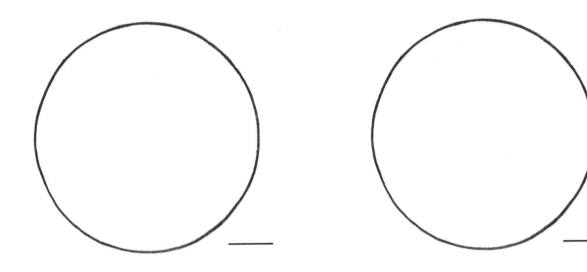

Time yourself. Be sure your drawing is complete within 15 seconds.
Jot down your time below. Be aware which drawings require more time.

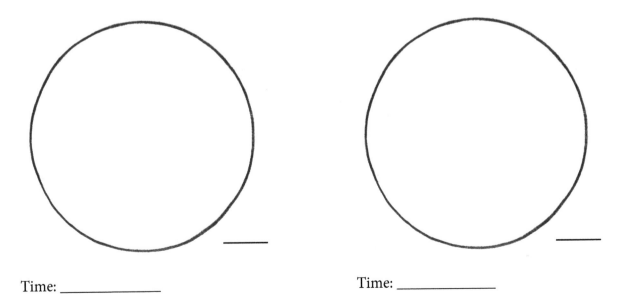

Time: _____

Time: _____

2.5

Orientation: Draw the icons you have learned in context. After your drawings are complete, express the meaning of each in sign language and then in spoken language.

____

____   ____

____   ____

____   2.6

2.5

2.0 PROFESSIONALISM

Tenet: Interpreters possess the professional skills and knowledge required for the specific interpreting situation.

Illustrative Behavior - Interpreters:

2.1 Provide service delivery regardless of race, color, national origin, gender, religion, age, disability, sexual orientation, or any other factor.

2.2 Assess consumer needs and the interpreting situation before and during the assignment and make adjustments as needed.

2.3 Render the message faithfully by conveying the content and spirit of what is being communicated, using language most readily understood by consumers, and correcting errors discreetly and expeditiously.

2.4 Request support (e.g., certified deaf interpreters, team members, language facilitators) when needed to fully convey the message or to address exceptional communication challenges (e.g. cognitive disabilities, foreign sign language, emerging language ability, or lack of formal instruction or language).

2.5 Refrain from providing counsel, advice, or personal opinions.

2.6 Judiciously provide information or referral regarding available interpreting or community resources without infringing upon consumers' rights.

2.6

2.6 Judiciously provide information or referral regarding available interpreting or community resources without infringing upon consumers' rights.

Explanation:

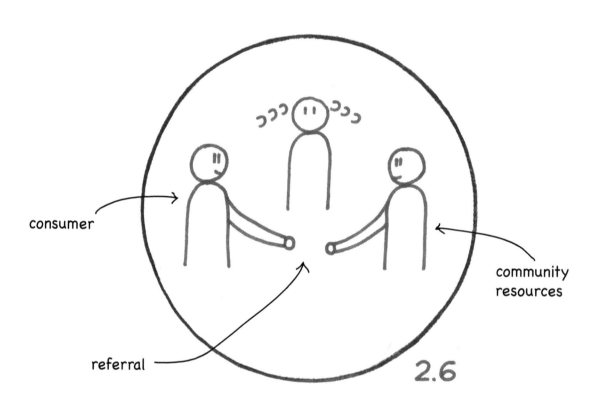

Imitation: Trace the image below.

2.6

Comprehension:

Expression: Draw with understanding.

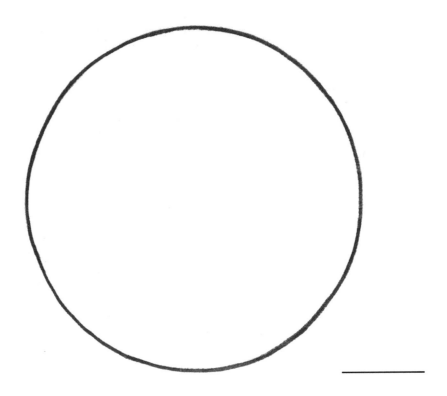

_____

Reflection: Make notes about the meaning.
Clarify your understanding or write down questions to address with a mentor.

_____

_____

_____

_____

_____

Memorization: Practice drawing without turning back to see the original.

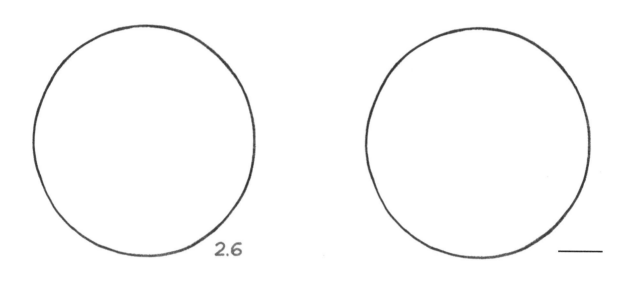

2.6

Check for accuracy. If you know it, save these others for future review.

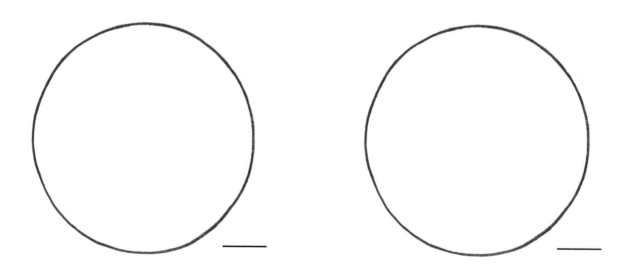

Acceleration: Practice drawing as quickly as possible.
Compare to original to ensure nothing was overlooked.

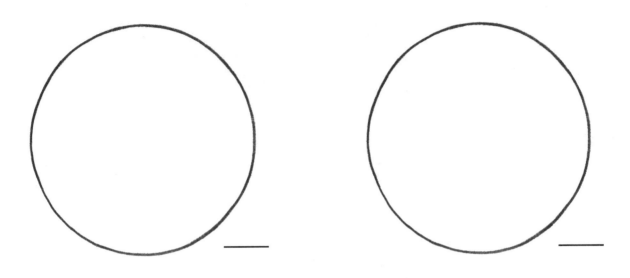

Time yourself. Be sure your drawing is complete within 15 seconds.
Jot down your time below. Be aware which drawings require more time.

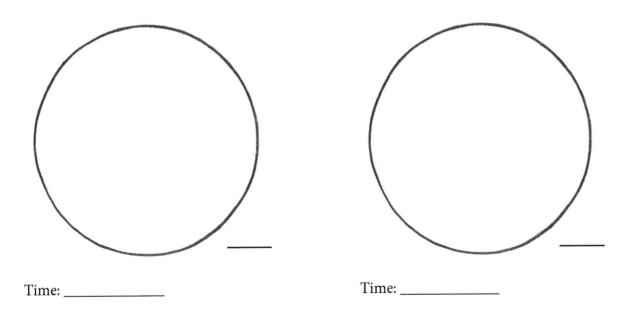

Time: _____   Time: _____

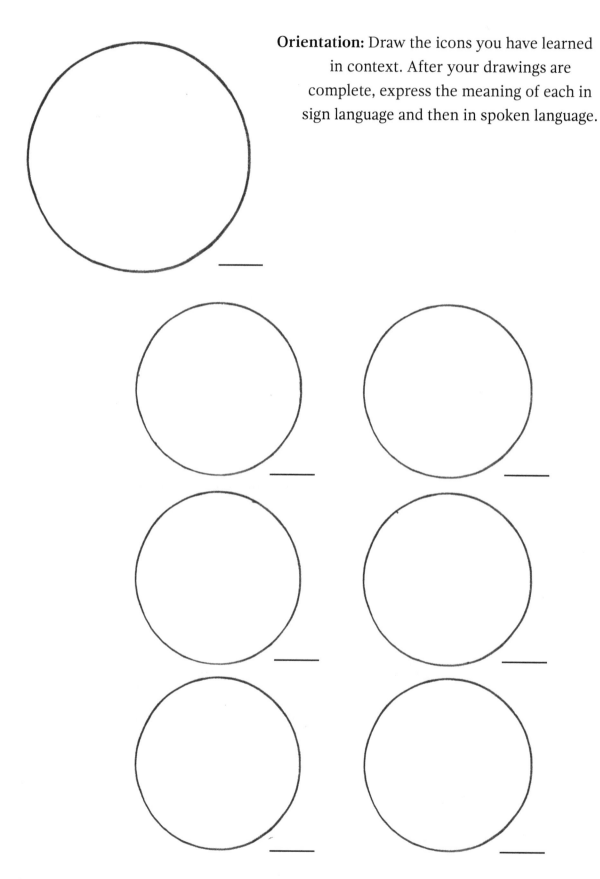

Orientation: Draw the icons you have learned in context. After your drawings are complete, express the meaning of each in sign language and then in spoken language.

2.6

3.0 CONDUCT

Tenet: Interpreters conduct themselves in a manner appropriate to the specific interpreting situation.

Illustrative Behavior - Interpreters:

3.1 Consult with appropriate persons regarding the interpreting situation to determine issues such as placement and adaptations necessary to interpret effectively.

3.2 Decline assignments or withdraw from the interpreting profession when not competent due to physical, mental, or emotional factors.

3.3 Avoid performing dual or conflicting roles in interdisciplinary (e.g. educational or mental health teams) or other settings.

3.4 Comply with established workplace codes of conduct, notify appropriate personnel if there is a conflict with this Code of Professional Conduct, and actively seek resolution where warranted.

3.5 Conduct and present themselves in an unobtrusive manner and exercise care in choice of attire.

3.6 Refrain from the use of mind-altering substances before or during the performance of duties.

3.7 Disclose to parties involved any actual or perceived conflicts of interest.

3.8 Avoid actual or perceived conflicts of interest that might cause harm or interfere with the effectiveness of interpreting services.

3.9 Refrain from using confidential interpreted information for personal, monetary, or professional gain.

3.10 Refrain from using confidential interpreted information for the benefit of personal or professional affiliations or entities.

3.0 Tenet: Interpreters conduct themselves in a manner appropriate to the specific interpreting situation.

Explanation:

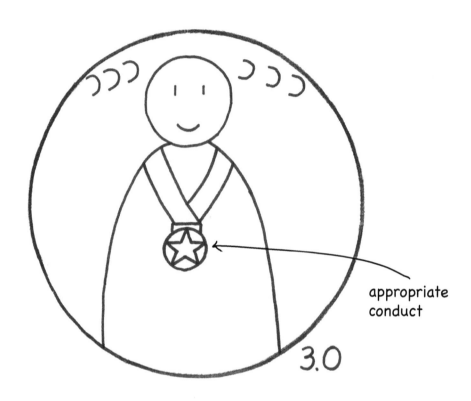

appropriate conduct

3.0

Imitation: Trace the image below.

Comprehension:

Expression: Draw with understanding.

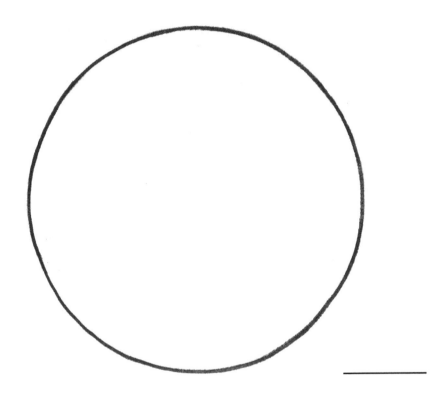

Reflection: Make notes about the meaning.
Clarify your understanding or write down questions to address with a mentor.

_____

_____

_____

_____

_____

Memorization: Practice drawing without turning back to see the original.

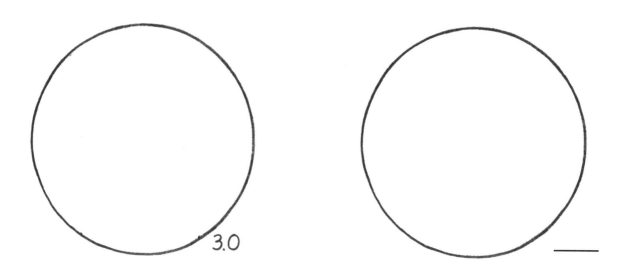

3.0

Check for accuracy. If you know it, save these others for future review.

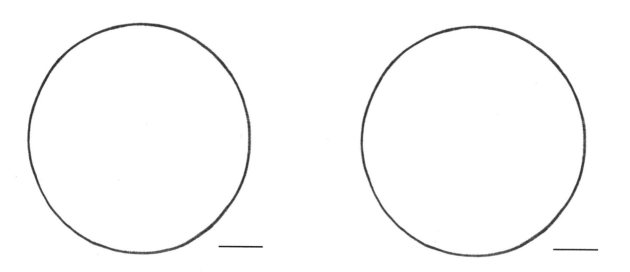

Acceleration: Practice drawing as quickly as possible.
Compare to original to ensure nothing was overlooked.

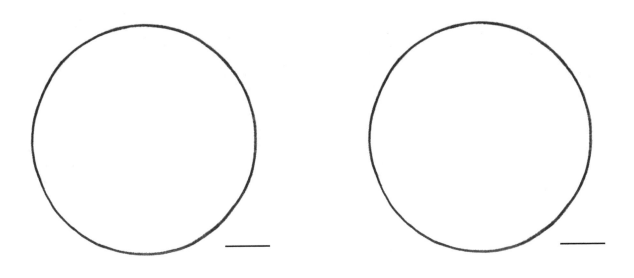

Time yourself. Be sure your drawing is complete within 15 seconds.
Jot down your time below. Be aware which drawings require more time.

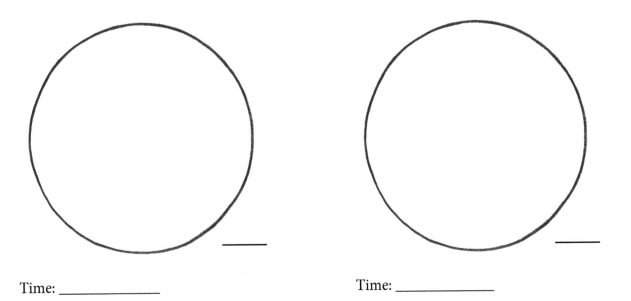

Time: _____

Time: _____

3.0

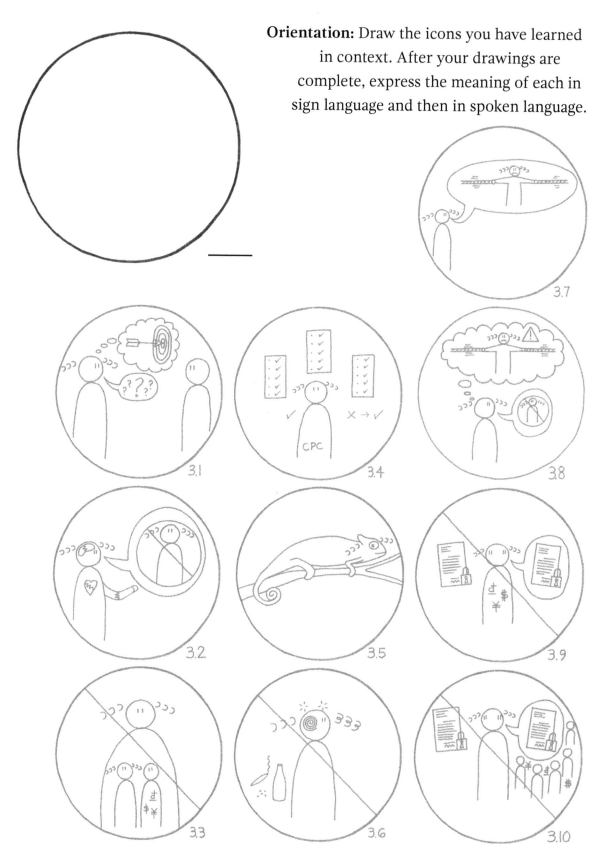

Orientation: Draw the icons you have learned in context. After your drawings are complete, express the meaning of each in sign language and then in spoken language.

3.0

3.0 CONDUCT

Tenet: Interpreters conduct themselves in a manner appropriate to the specific interpreting situation.

Illustrative Behavior - Interpreters:

3.1 Consult with appropriate persons regarding the interpreting situation to determine issues such as placement and adaptations necessary to interpret effectively.

3.2 Decline assignments or withdraw from the interpreting profession when not competent due to physical, mental, or emotional factors.

3.3 Avoid performing dual or conflicting roles in interdisciplinary (e.g. educational or mental health teams) or other settings.

3.4 Comply with established workplace codes of conduct, notify appropriate personnel if there is a conflict with this Code of Professional Conduct, and actively seek resolution where warranted.

3.5 Conduct and present themselves in an unobtrusive manner and exercise care in choice of attire.

3.6 Refrain from the use of mind-altering substances before or during the performance of duties.

3.7 Disclose to parties involved any actual or perceived conflicts of interest.

3.8 Avoid actual or perceived conflicts of interest that might cause harm or interfere with the effectiveness of interpreting services.

3.9 Refrain from using confidential interpreted information for personal, monetary, or professional gain.

3.10 Refrain from using confidential interpreted information for the benefit of personal or professional affiliations or entities.

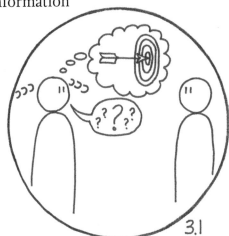

3.1

3.1 Consult with appropriate persons regarding the interpreting situation to determine issues such as placement and adaptations necessary to interpret effectively.

Explanation:

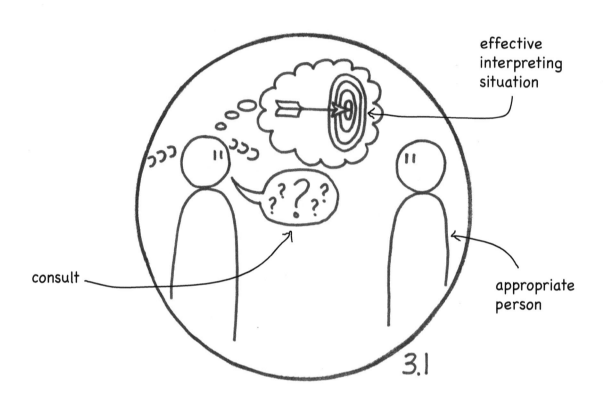

Imitation: Trace the image below.

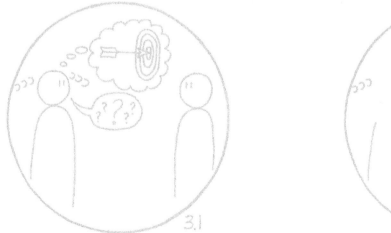

3.1

Comprehension:

Expression: Draw with understanding.

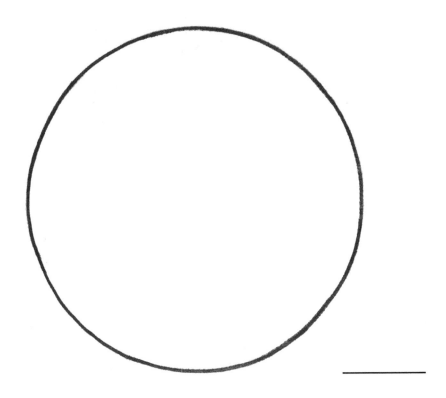

Reflection: Make notes about the meaning.
Clarify your understanding or write down questions to address with a mentor.

_____

_____

_____

_____

_____

Memorization: Practice drawing without turning back to see the original.

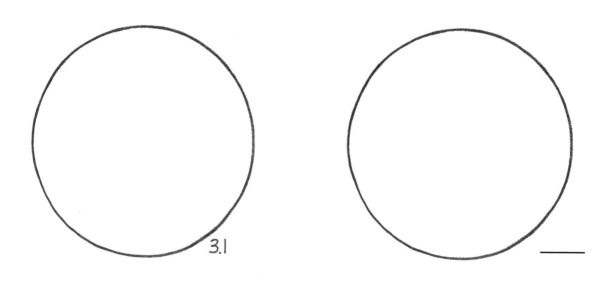

3.1

Check for accuracy. If you know it, save these others for future review.

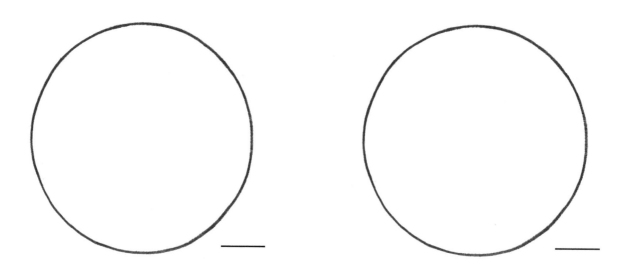

Acceleration: Practice drawing as quickly as possible.
Compare to original to ensure nothing was overlooked.

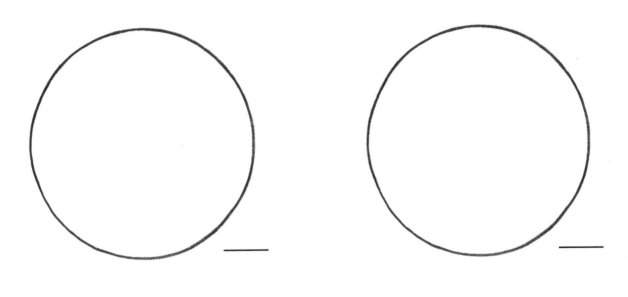

Time yourself. Be sure your drawing is complete within 15 seconds.
Jot down your time below. Be aware which drawings require more time.

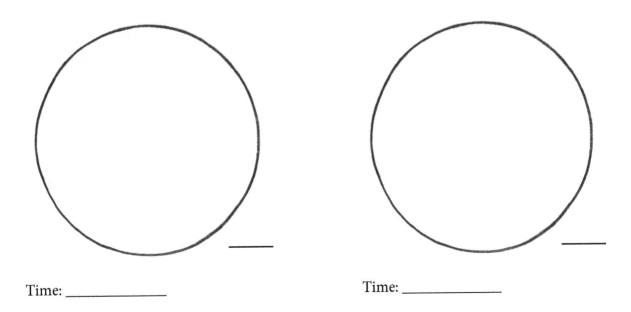

Time: _____   Time: _____

3.1

Orientation: Draw the icons you have learned in context. After your drawings are complete, express the meaning of each in sign language and then in spoken language.

3.1

3.2

3.3

3.4

3.5

3.6

3.7

3.8

3.9

3.10

3.0 CONDUCT

Tenet: Interpreters conduct themselves in a manner appropriate to the specific interpreting situation.

Illustrative Behavior - Interpreters:

3.1 Consult with appropriate persons regarding the interpreting situation to determine issues such as placement and adaptations necessary to interpret effectively.

3.2 **Decline assignments or withdraw from the interpreting profession when not competent due to physical, mental, or emotional factors.**

3.3 Avoid performing dual or conflicting roles in interdisciplinary (e.g. educational or mental health teams) or other settings.

3.4 Comply with established workplace codes of conduct, notify appropriate personnel if there is a conflict with this Code of Professional Conduct, and actively seek resolution where warranted.

3.5 Conduct and present themselves in an unobtrusive manner and exercise care in choice of attire.

3.6 Refrain from the use of mind-altering substances before or during the performance of duties.

3.7 Disclose to parties involved any actual or perceived conflicts of interest.

3.8 Avoid actual or perceived conflicts of interest that might cause harm or interfere with the effectiveness of interpreting services.

3.9 Refrain from using confidential interpreted information for personal, monetary, or professional gain.

3.10 Refrain from using confidential interpreted information for the benefit of personal or professional affiliations or entities.

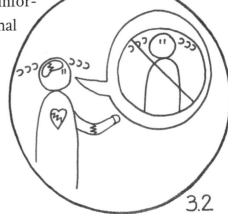

3.2

3.2 Decline assignments or withdraw from the interpreting profession when not competent due to physical, mental, or emotional factors.

Explanation:

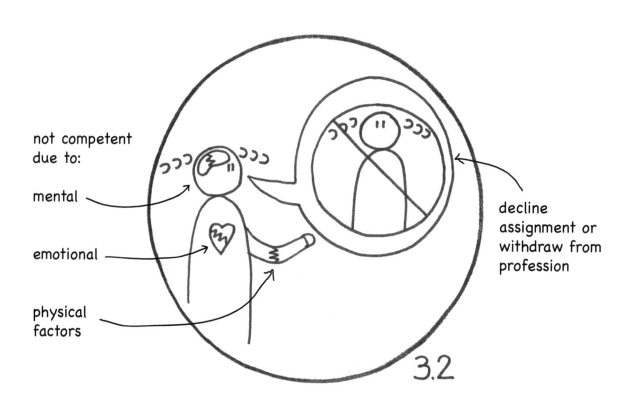

Imitation: Trace the image below.

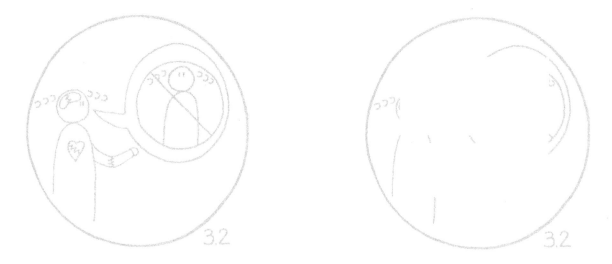

Comprehension:

Expression: Draw with understanding.

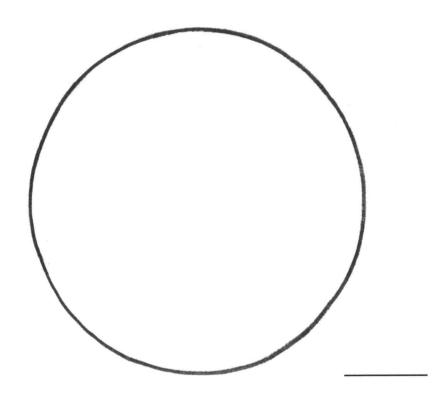

Reflection: Make notes about the meaning.

Clarify your understanding or write down questions to address with a mentor.

_____

_____

_____

_____

_____

Memorization: Practice drawing without turning back to see the original.

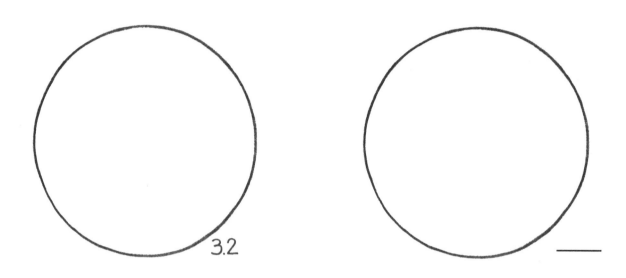

3.2

Check for accuracy. If you know it, save these others for future review.

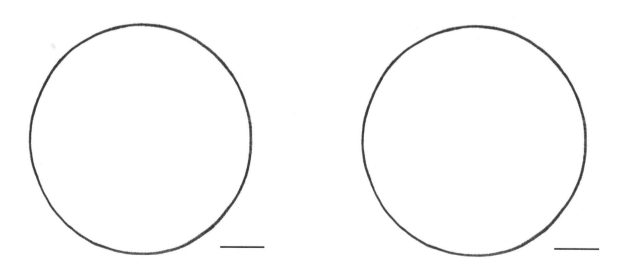

Acceleration: Practice drawing as quickly as possible.
Compare to original to ensure nothing was overlooked.

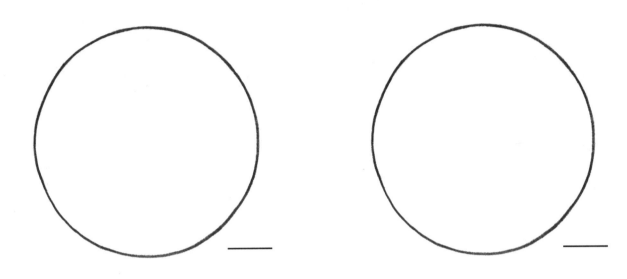

Time yourself. Be sure your drawing is complete within 15 seconds.
Jot down your time below. Be aware which drawings require more time.

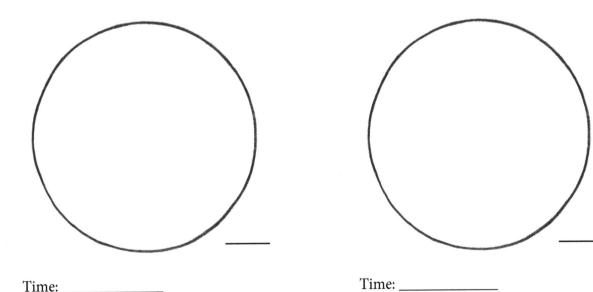

Time: _____   Time: _____

Orientation: Draw the icons you have learned in context. After your drawings are complete, express the meaning of each in sign language and then in spoken language.

3.7

3.4

3.8

3.5

3.9

3.3

3.6

3.10

3.2

3.0 CONDUCT

Tenet: Interpreters conduct themselves in a manner appropriate to the specific interpreting situation.

Illustrative Behavior - Interpreters:

3.1 Consult with appropriate persons regarding the interpreting situation to determine issues such as placement and adaptations necessary to interpret effectively.

3.2 Decline assignments or withdraw from the interpreting profession when not competent due to physical, mental, or emotional factors.

3.3 Avoid performing dual or conflicting roles in interdisciplinary (e.g. educational or mental health teams) or other settings.

3.4 Comply with established workplace codes of conduct, notify appropriate personnel if there is a conflict with this Code of Professional Conduct, and actively seek resolution where warranted.

3.5 Conduct and present themselves in an unobtrusive manner and exercise care in choice of attire.

3.6 Refrain from the use of mind-altering substances before or during the performance of duties.

3.7 Disclose to parties involved any actual or perceived conflicts of interest.

3.8 Avoid actual or perceived conflicts of interest that might cause harm or interfere with the effectiveness of interpreting services.

3.9 Refrain from using confidential interpreted information for personal, monetary, or professional gain.

3.10 Refrain from using confidential interpreted information for the benefit of personal or professional affiliations or entities.

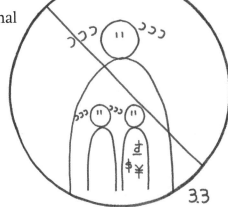

3.3 Avoid performing dual or conflicting roles in interdisciplinary or other settings.

Explanation:

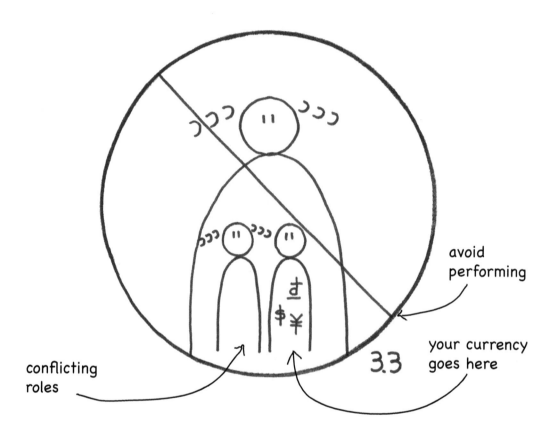

avoid performing

conflicting roles

your currency goes here

Imitation: Trace the image below.

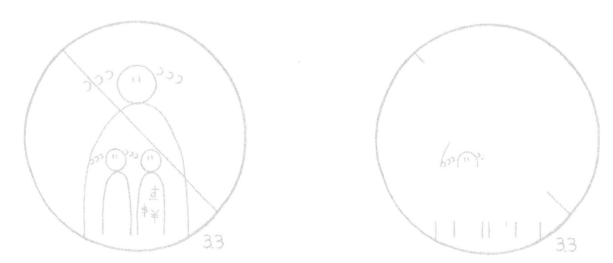

Comprehension:

Expression: Draw with understanding.

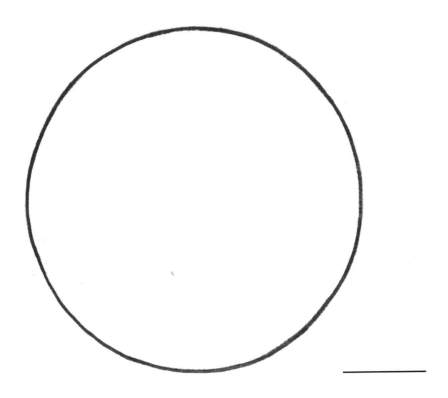

_____

Reflection: Make notes about the meaning.

Clarify your understanding or write down questions to address with a mentor.

_____

_____

_____

_____

Memorization: Practice drawing without turning back to see the original.

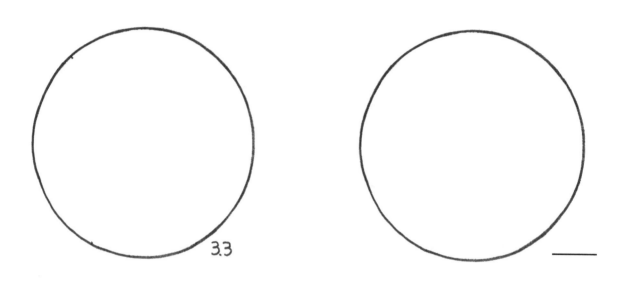

3.3

Check for accuracy. If you know it, save these others for future review.

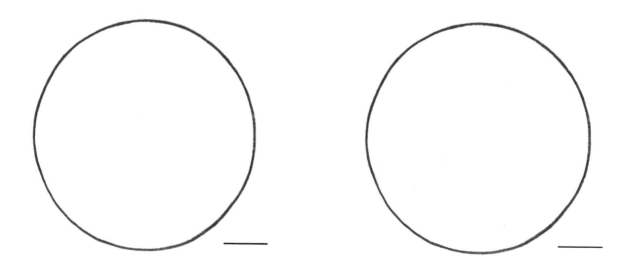

Acceleration: Practice drawing as quickly as possible.
Compare to original to ensure nothing was overlooked.

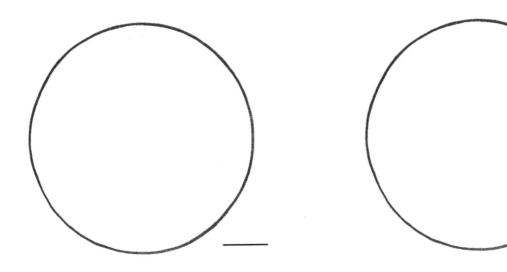

Time yourself. Be sure your drawing is complete within 15 seconds.
Jot down your time below. Be aware which drawings require more time.

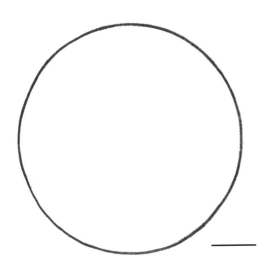

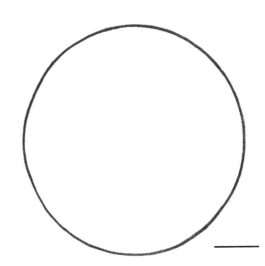

Time: _____

Time: _____

3.3

Orientation: Draw the icons you have learned in context. After your drawings are complete, express the meaning of each in sign language and then in spoken language.

3.7

3.4

3.8

3.5

3.9

3.6

3.10

CPC

3.3

3.0 CONDUCT

Tenet: Interpreters conduct themselves in a manner appropriate to the specific interpreting situation.

Illustrative Behavior - Interpreters:

3.1 Consult with appropriate persons regarding the interpreting situation to determine issues such as placement and adaptations necessary to interpret effectively.

3.2 Decline assignments or withdraw from the interpreting profession when not competent due to physical, mental, or emotional factors.

3.3 Avoid performing dual or conflicting roles in interdisciplinary (e.g. educational or mental health teams) or other settings.

3.4 Comply with established workplace codes of conduct, notify appropriate personnel if there is a conflict with this Code of Professional Conduct, and actively seek resolution where warranted.

3.5 Conduct and present themselves in an unobtrusive manner and exercise care in choice of attire.

3.6 Refrain from the use of mind-altering substances before or during the performance of duties.

3.7 Disclose to parties involved any actual or perceived conflicts of interest.

3.8 Avoid actual or perceived conflicts of interest that might cause harm or interfere with the effectiveness of interpreting services.

3.9 Refrain from using confidential interpreted information for personal, monetary, or professional gain.

3.10 Refrain from using confidential interpreted information for the benefit of personal or professional affiliations or entities.

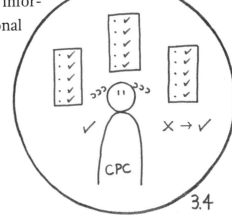

3.4 Comply with established workplace codes of conduct, notify appropriate personnel if there is a conflict with this Code of Professional Conduct, and actively seek resolution where warranted.

Explanation:

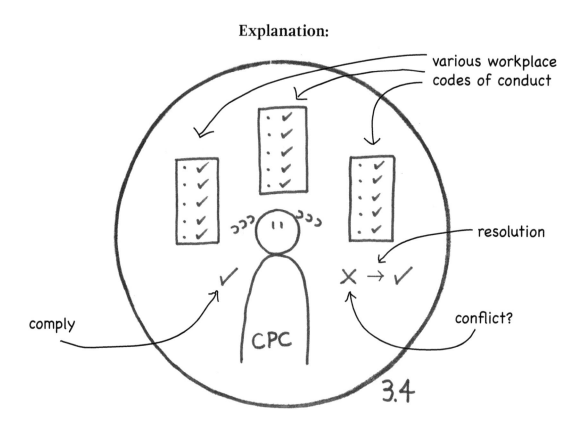

Imitation: Trace the image below.

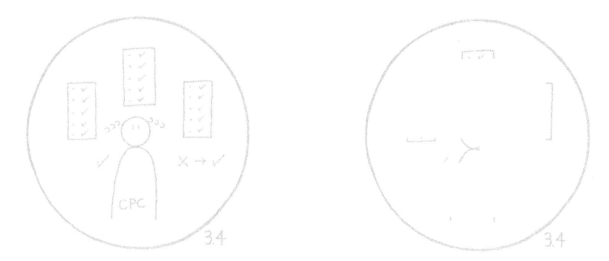

Comprehension:

Expression: Draw with understanding.

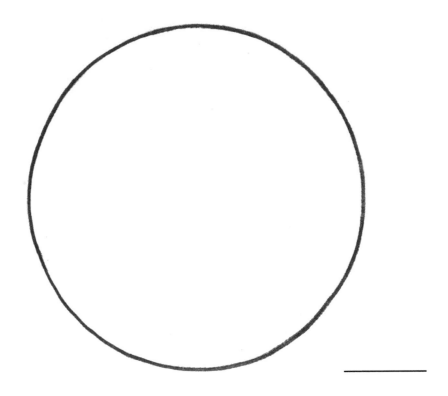

_____

Reflection: Make notes about the meaning.
Clarify your understanding or write down questions to address with a mentor.

_____

_____

_____

_____

_____

Memorization: Practice drawing without turning back to see the original.

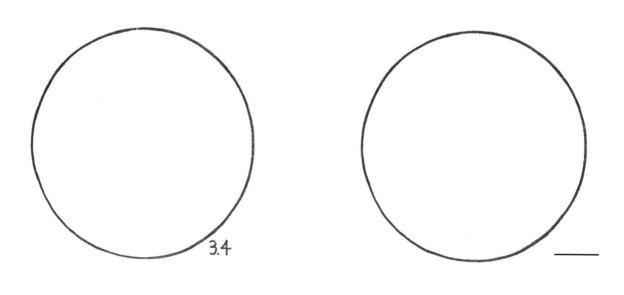

3.4

Check for accuracy. If you know it, save these others for future review.

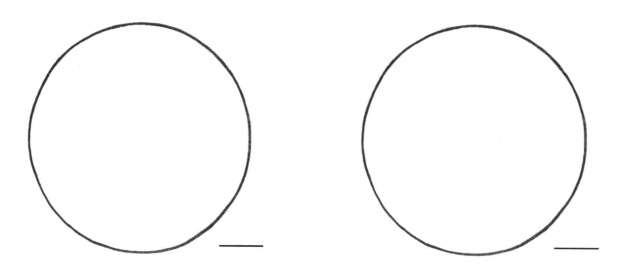

Acceleration: Practice drawing as quickly as possible.
Compare to original to ensure nothing was overlooked.

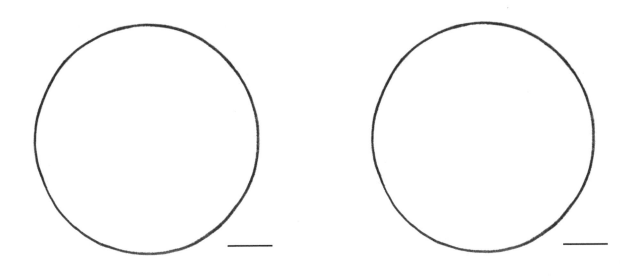

Time yourself. Be sure your drawing is complete within 15 seconds.
Jot down your time below. Be aware which drawings require more time.

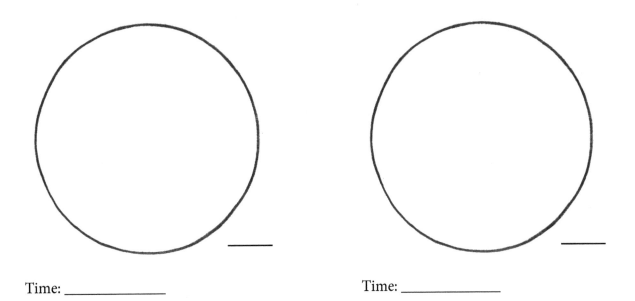

Time: _____   Time: _____

3.4

Orientation: Draw the icons you have learned in context. After your drawings are complete, express the meaning of each in sign language and then in spoken language.

3.7

3.8

3.5

3.9

3.6

3.10

3.0 CONDUCT

Tenet: Interpreters conduct themselves in a manner appropriate to the specific interpreting situation.

Illustrative Behavior - Interpreters:

3.1 Consult with appropriate persons regarding the interpreting situation to determine issues such as placement and adaptations necessary to interpret effectively.

3.2 Decline assignments or withdraw from the interpreting profession when not competent due to physical, mental, or emotional factors.

3.3 Avoid performing dual or conflicting roles in interdisciplinary (e.g. educational or mental health teams) or other settings.

3.4 Comply with established workplace codes of conduct, notify appropriate personnel if there is a conflict with this Code of Professional Conduct, and actively seek resolution where warranted.

3.5 Conduct and present themselves in an unobtrusive manner and exercise care in choice of attire.

3.6 Refrain from the use of mind-altering substances before or during the performance of duties.

3.7 Disclose to parties involved any actual or perceived conflicts of interest.

3.8 Avoid actual or perceived conflicts of interest that might cause harm or interfere with the effectiveness of interpreting services.

3.9 Refrain from using confidential interpreted information for personal, monetary, or professional gain.

3.10 Refrain from using confidential interpreted information for the benefit of personal or professional affiliations or entities.

3.5

3.5 Conduct and present themselves in an unobtrusive manner
and exercise care in choice of attire.

Explanation:

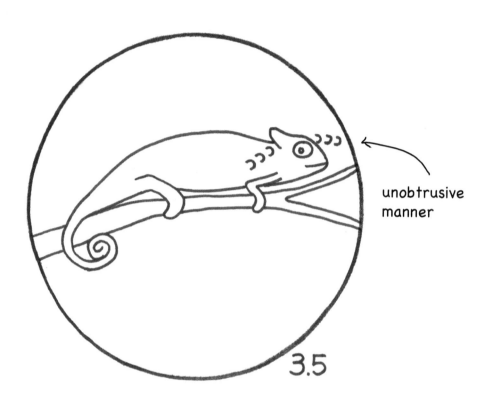

unobtrusive
manner

3.5

Imitation: Trace the image below.

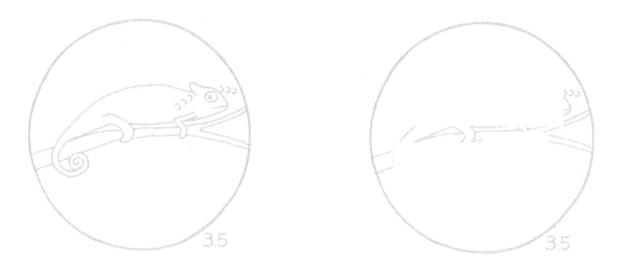

Comprehension:

Expression: Draw with understanding.

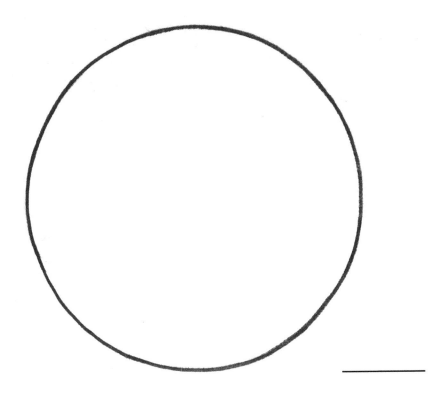

Reflection: Make notes about the meaning.

Clarify your understanding or write down questions to address with a mentor.

Memorization: Practice drawing without turning back to see the original.

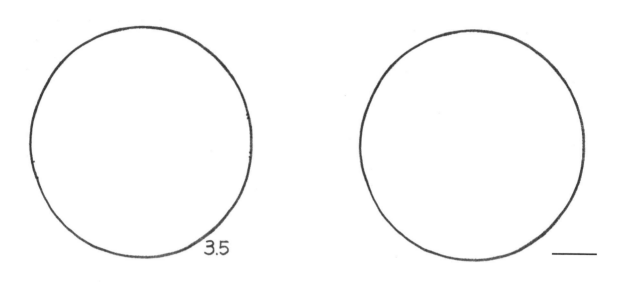

3.5

Check for accuracy. If you know it, save these others for future review.

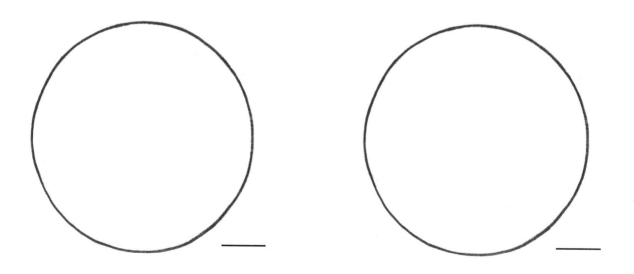

Acceleration: Practice drawing as quickly as possible.
Compare to original to ensure nothing was overlooked.

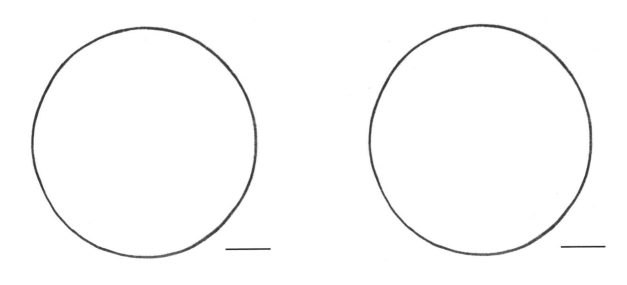

Time yourself. Be sure your drawing is complete within 15 seconds.
Jot down your time below. Be aware which drawings require more time.

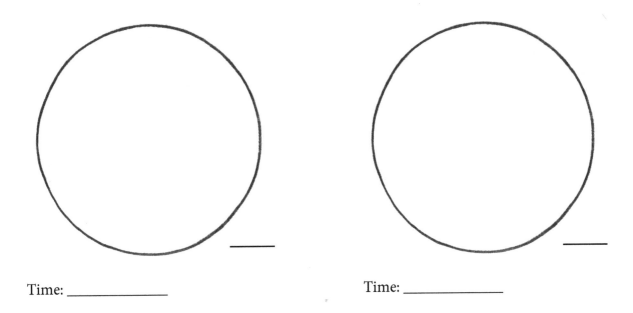

Time: _____   Time: _____

3.5

Orientation: Draw the icons you have learned in context. After your drawings are complete, express the meaning of each in sign language and then in spoken language.

3.7

3.8

3.9

3.6

3.10

3.5

3.0 CONDUCT

Tenet: Interpreters conduct themselves in a manner appropriate to the specific interpreting situation.

Illustrative Behavior - Interpreters:

3.1 Consult with appropriate persons regarding the interpreting situation to determine issues such as placement and adaptations necessary to interpret effectively.

3.2 Decline assignments or withdraw from the interpreting profession when not
competent due to physical, mental, or emotional factors.

3.3 Avoid performing dual or conflicting roles in interdisciplinary (e.g. educational
or mental health teams) or other settings.

3.4 Comply with established workplace codes of conduct, notify appropriate personnel if there is a conflict with this Code of Professional Conduct, and actively seek
resolution where warranted.

3.5 Conduct and present themselves in an unobtrusive manner and exercise care in
choice of attire.

3.6 **Refrain from the use of mind-altering substances before or during the performance of duties.**

3.7 Disclose to parties involved any actual or perceived conflicts of interest.

3.8 Avoid actual or perceived conflicts of interest that might cause harm or interfere
with the effectiveness of interpreting services.

3.9 Refrain from using confidential interpreted information for personal, monetary,
or professional gain.

3.10 Refrain from using confidential interpreted information for the benefit of personal or professional
affiliations or entities.

3.6

3.6 Refrain from the use of mind-altering substances before or
during the performance of duties.

Explanation:

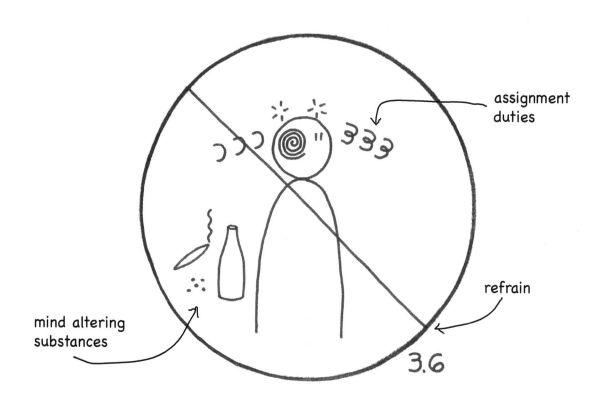

Imitation: Trace the image below.

Comprehension:

Expression: Draw with understanding.

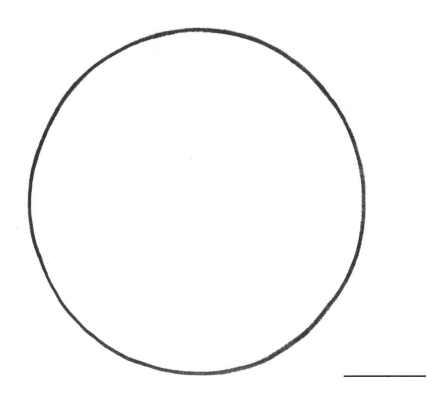

Reflection: Make notes about the meaning.
Clarify your understanding or write down questions to address with a mentor.

_____

_____

_____

_____

_____

Memorization: Practice drawing without turning back to see the original.

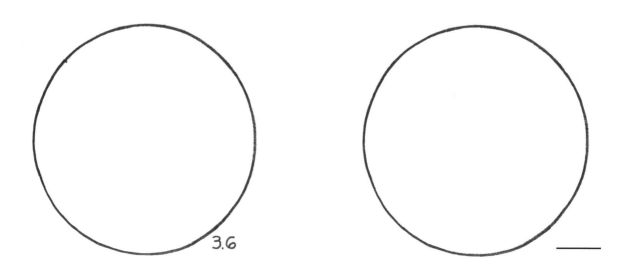

3.6

Check for accuracy. If you know it, save these others for future review.

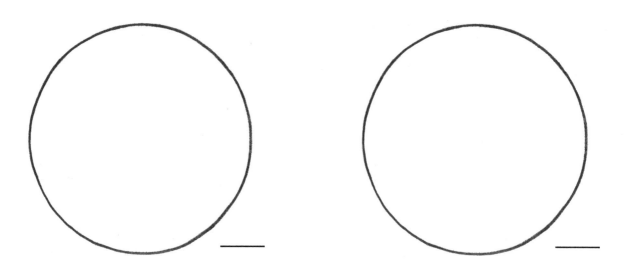

Acceleration: Practice drawing as quickly as possible.
Compare to original to ensure nothing was overlooked.

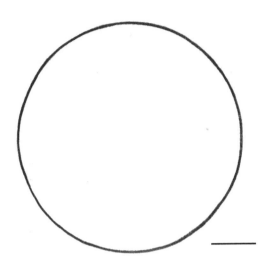 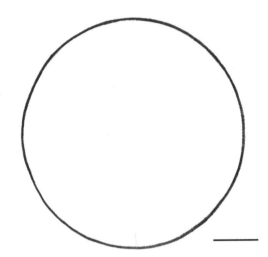

Time yourself. Be sure your drawing is complete within 15 seconds.
Jot down your time below. Be aware which drawings require more time.

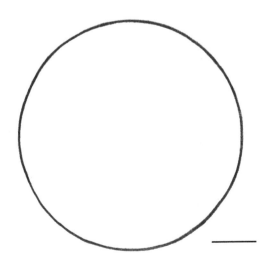 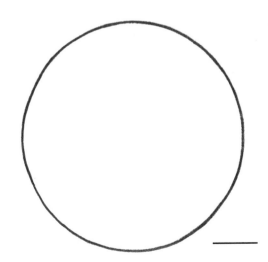

Time: _____   Time: _____

3.6

Orientation: Draw the icons you have learned in context. After your drawings are complete, express the meaning of each in sign language and then in spoken language.

3.7

3.8

3.9

3.10

3.6

3.0 CONDUCT

Tenet: Interpreters conduct themselves in a manner appropriate to the specific interpreting situation.

Illustrative Behavior - Interpreters:

3.1 Consult with appropriate persons regarding the interpreting situation to determine issues such as placement and adaptations necessary to interpret effectively.

3.2 Decline assignments or withdraw from the interpreting profession when not competent due to physical, mental, or emotional factors.

3.3 Avoid performing dual or conflicting roles in interdisciplinary (e.g. educational or mental health teams) or other settings.

3.4 Comply with established workplace codes of conduct, notify appropriate personnel if there is a conflict with this Code of Professional Conduct, and actively seek resolution where warranted.

3.5 Conduct and present themselves in an unobtrusive manner and exercise care in choice of attire.

3.6 Refrain from the use of mind-altering substances before or during the performance of duties.

3.7 Disclose to parties involved any actual or perceived conflicts of interest.

3.8 Avoid actual or perceived conflicts of interest that might cause harm or interfere with the effectiveness of interpreting services.

3.9 Refrain from using confidential interpreted information for personal, monetary, or professional gain.

3.10 Refrain from using confidential interpreted information for the benefit of personal or professional affiliations or entities.

3.7

3.7 Disclose to parties involved any actual or perceived conflicts of interest.

Explanation:

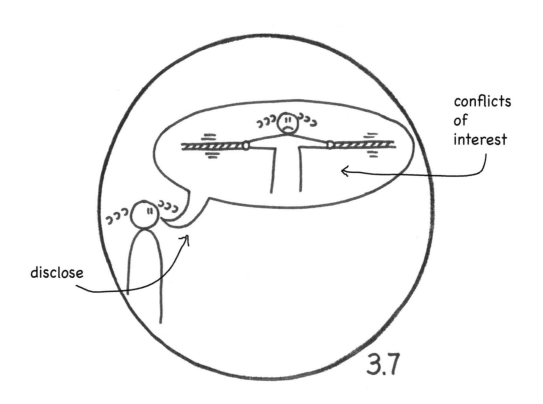

Imitation: Trace the image below.

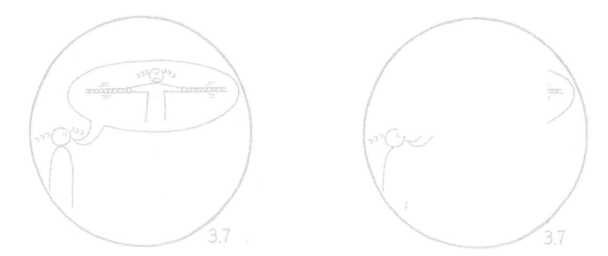

Comprehension:

Expression: Draw with understanding.

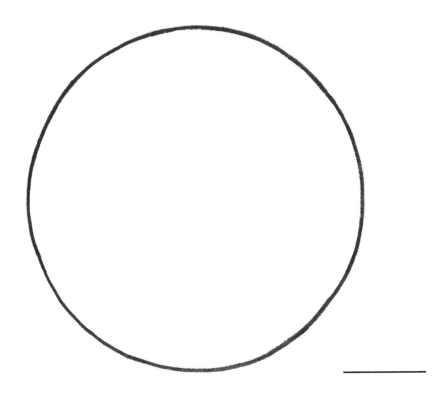

_____

Reflection: Make notes about the meaning.
Clarify your understanding or write down questions to address with a mentor.

_____

_____

_____

_____

_____

Memorization: Practice drawing without turning back to see the original.

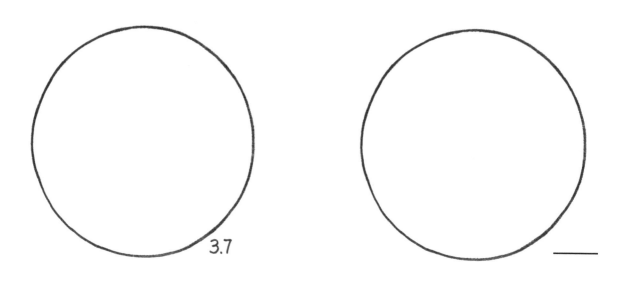

3.7

Check for accuracy. If you know it, save these others for future review.

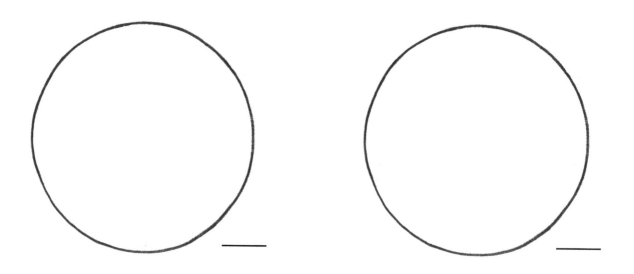

Acceleration: Practice drawing as quickly as possible.
Compare to original to ensure nothing was overlooked.

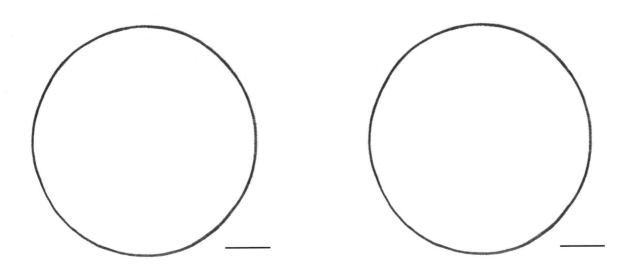

Time yourself. Be sure your drawing is complete within 15 seconds.
Jot down your time below. Be aware which drawings require more time.

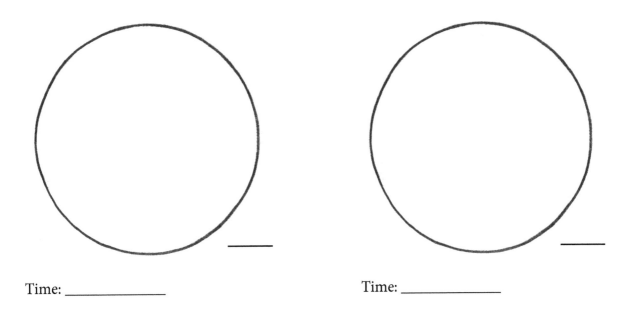

Time: _____

Time: _____

Orientation: Draw the icons you have learned in context. After your drawings are complete, express the meaning of each in sign language and then in spoken language.

3.8

3.9

3.10

3.0 CONDUCT

Tenet: Interpreters conduct themselves in a manner appropriate to the specific interpreting situation.

Illustrative Behavior - Interpreters:

3.1 Consult with appropriate persons regarding the interpreting situation to determine issues such as placement and adaptations necessary to interpret effectively.

3.2 Decline assignments or withdraw from the interpreting profession when not competent due to physical, mental, or emotional factors.

3.3 Avoid performing dual or conflicting roles in interdisciplinary (e.g. educational or mental health teams) or other settings.

3.4 Comply with established workplace codes of conduct, notify appropriate personnel if there is a conflict with this Code of Professional Conduct, and actively seek resolution where warranted.

3.5 Conduct and present themselves in an unobtrusive manner and exercise care in choice of attire.

3.6 Refrain from the use of mind-altering substances before or during the performance of duties.

3.7 Disclose to parties involved any actual or perceived conflicts of interest.

3.8 **Avoid actual or perceived conflicts of interest that might cause harm or interfere with the effectiveness of interpreting services.**

3.9 Refrain from using confidential interpreted information for personal, monetary, or professional gain.

3.10 Refrain from using confidential interpreted information for the benefit of personal or professional affiliations or entities.

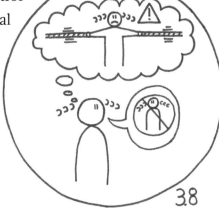

3.8

3.8 Avoid actual or perceived conflicts of interest that might cause harm or interfere with the effectiveness of interpreting services.

Explanation:

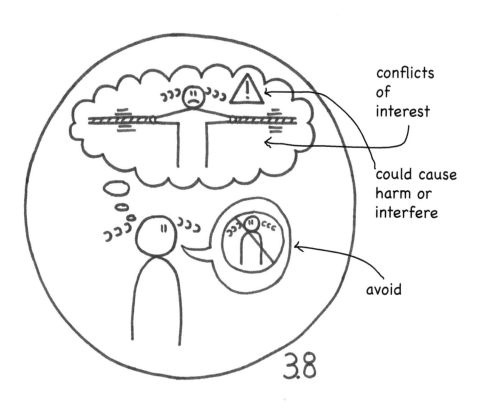

conflicts of interest

could cause harm or interfere

avoid

Imitation: Trace the image below.

Comprehension:

Expression: Draw with understanding.

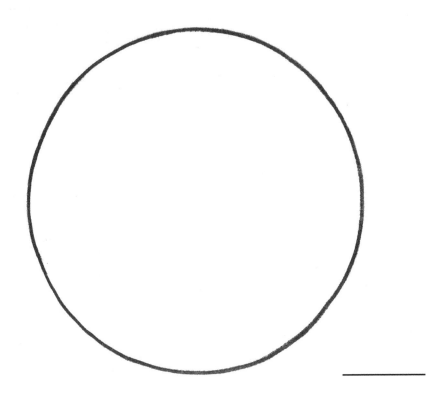

_____

Reflection: Make notes about the meaning.
Clarify your understanding or write down questions to address with a mentor.

_____

_____

_____

_____

_____

Memorization: Practice drawing without turning back to see the original.

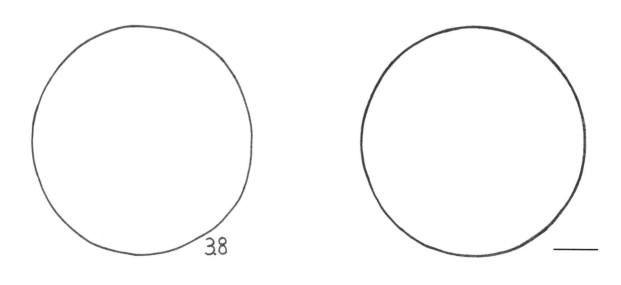

3.8

Check for accuracy. If you know it, save these others for future review.

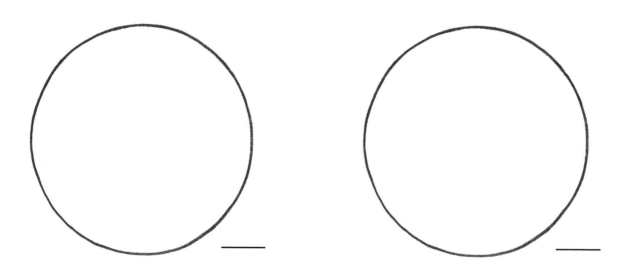

Acceleration: Practice drawing as quickly as possible.
Compare to original to ensure nothing was overlooked.

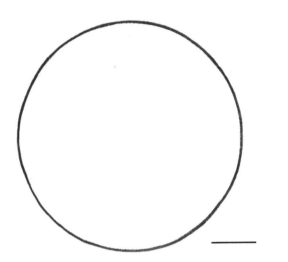 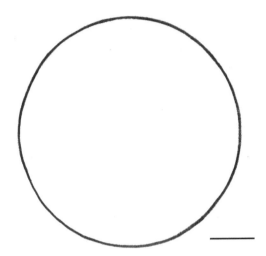

Time yourself. Be sure your drawing is complete within 15 seconds.
Jot down your time below. Be aware which drawings require more time.

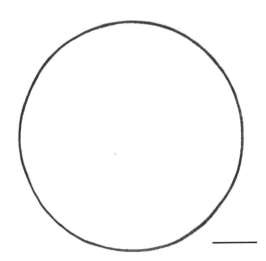 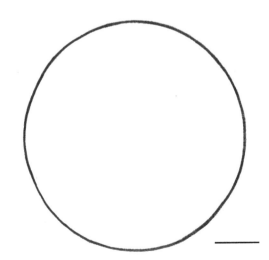

Time: _____   Time: _____

Orientation: Draw the icons you have learned in context. After your drawings are complete, express the meaning of each in sign language and then in spoken language.

3.9

3.10

3.0 CONDUCT

Tenet: Interpreters conduct themselves in a manner appropriate to the specific interpreting situation.

Illustrative Behavior - Interpreters:

3.1 Consult with appropriate persons regarding the interpreting situation to determine issues such as placement and adaptations necessary to interpret effectively.

3.2 Decline assignments or withdraw from the interpreting profession when not competent due to physical, mental, or emotional factors.

3.3 Avoid performing dual or conflicting roles in interdisciplinary (e.g. educational or mental health teams) or other settings.

3.4 Comply with established workplace codes of conduct, notify appropriate personnel if there is a conflict with this Code of Professional Conduct, and actively seek resolution where warranted.

3.5 Conduct and present themselves in an unobtrusive manner and exercise care in choice of attire.

3.6 Refrain from the use of mind-altering substances before or during the performance of duties.

3.7 Disclose to parties involved any actual or perceived conflicts of interest.

3.8 Avoid actual or perceived conflicts of interest that might cause harm or interfere with the effectiveness of interpreting services.

3.9 **Refrain from using confidential interpreted information for personal, monetary, or professional gain.**

3.10 Refrain from using confidential interpreted information for the benefit of personal or professional affiliations or entities.

3.9

3.9 Refrain from using confidential interpreted information for personal, monetary, or professional gain.

Explanation:

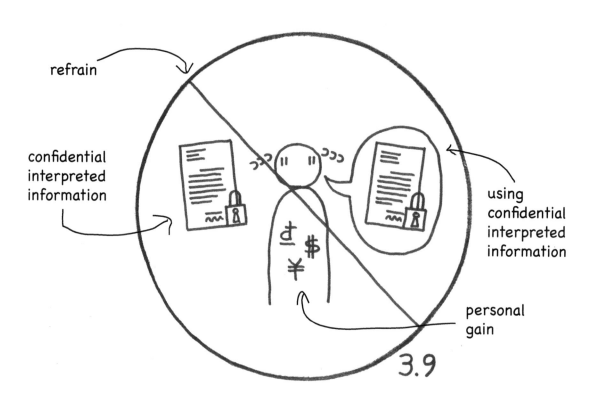

Imitation: Trace the image below.

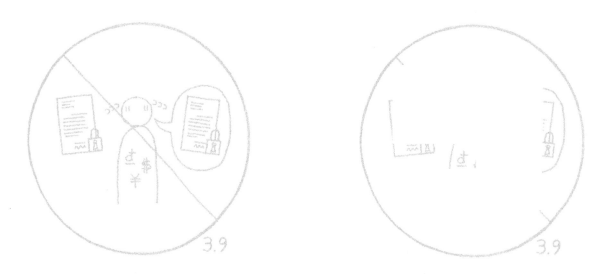

3.9

Comprehension:

Expression: Draw with understanding.

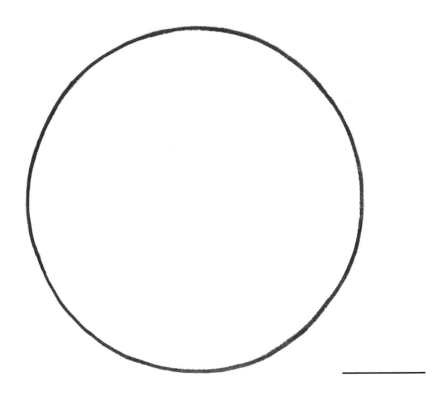

Reflection: Make notes about the meaning.

Clarify your understanding or write down questions to address with a mentor.

_____

_____

_____

_____

_____

3.9

Memorization: Practice drawing without turning back to see the original.

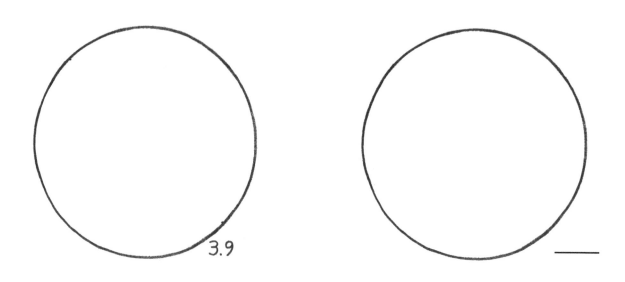

3.9

Check for accuracy. If you know it, save these others for future review.

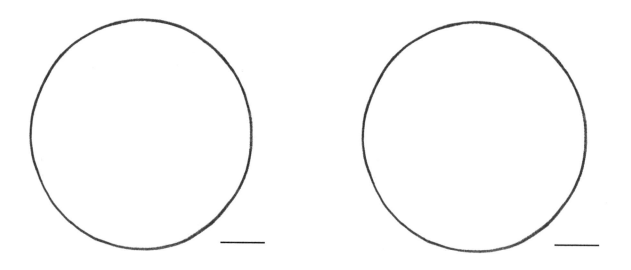

Acceleration: Practice drawing as quickly as possible.
Compare to original to ensure nothing was overlooked.

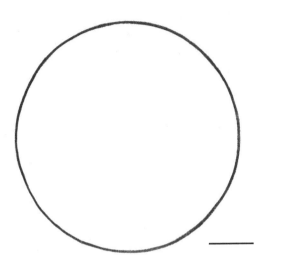

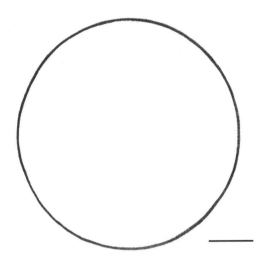

Time yourself. Be sure your drawing is complete within 15 seconds.
Jot down your time below. Be aware which drawings require more time.

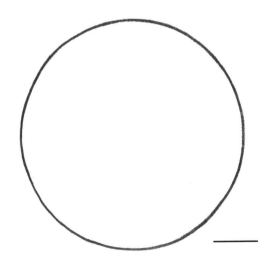

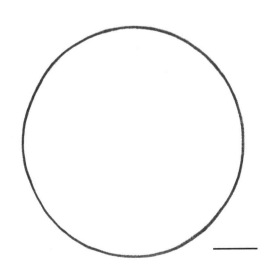

Time: _____

Time: _____

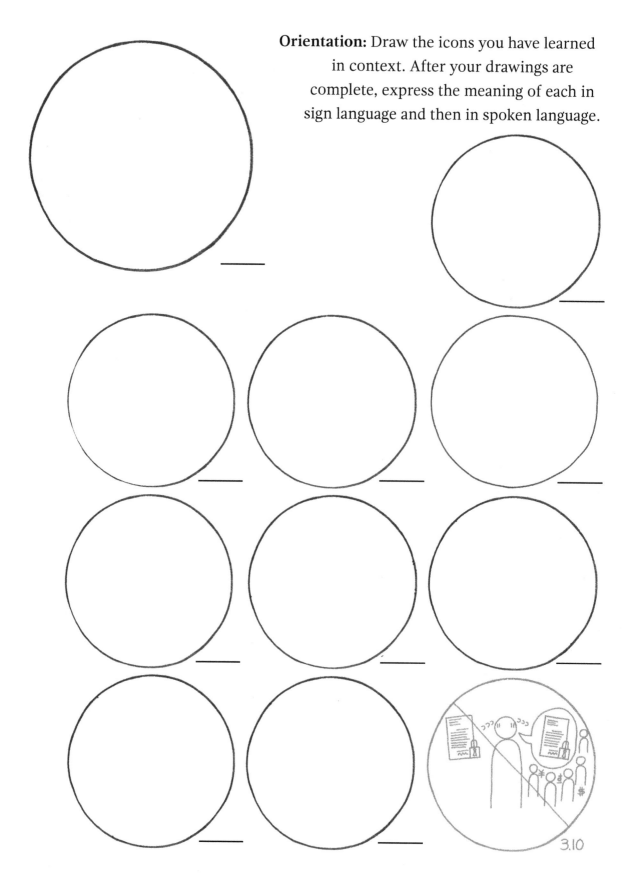

Orientation: Draw the icons you have learned in context. After your drawings are complete, express the meaning of each in sign language and then in spoken language.

3.10

3.9

3.0 CONDUCT

Tenet: Interpreters conduct themselves in a manner appropriate to the specific interpreting situation.

Illustrative Behavior - Interpreters:

3.1 Consult with appropriate persons regarding the interpreting situation to determine issues such as placement and adaptations necessary to interpret effectively.

3.2 Decline assignments or withdraw from the interpreting profession when not competent due to physical, mental, or emotional factors.

3.3 Avoid performing dual or conflicting roles in interdisciplinary (e.g. educational or mental health teams) or other settings.

3.4 Comply with established workplace codes of conduct, notify appropriate personnel if there is a conflict with this Code of Professional Conduct, and actively seek resolution where warranted.

3.5 Conduct and present themselves in an unobtrusive manner and exercise care in choice of attire.

3.6 Refrain from the use of mind-altering substances before or during the performance of duties.

3.7 Disclose to parties involved any actual or perceived conflicts of interest.

3.8 Avoid actual or perceived conflicts of interest that might cause harm or interfere with the effectiveness of interpreting services.

3.9 Refrain from using confidential interpreted information for personal, monetary, or professional gain.

3.10 **Refrain from using confidential interpreted information for the benefit of personal or professional affiliations or entities.**

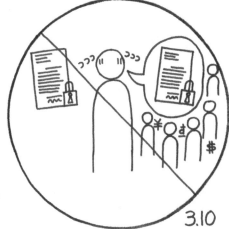

3.10

3.10 Refrain from using confidential interpreted information for the benefit of personal or professional affiliations or entities.

Explanation:

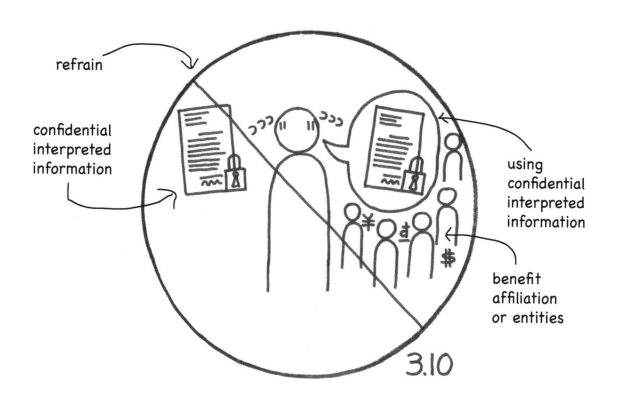

Imitation: Trace the image below.

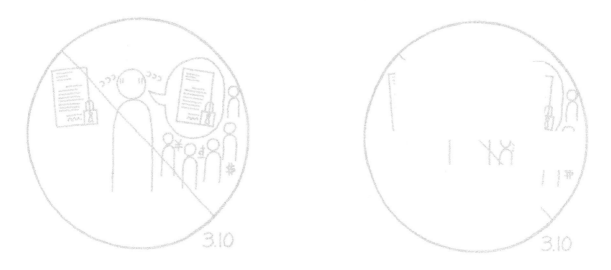

Comprehension:

Expression: Draw with understanding.

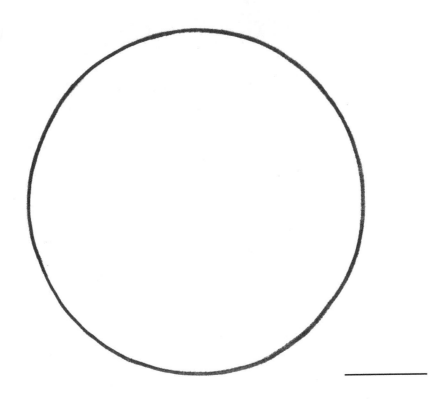

_____

Reflection: Make notes about the meaning.

Clarify your understanding or write down questions to address with a mentor.

_____

_____

_____

_____

_____

Memorization: Practice drawing without turning back to see the original.

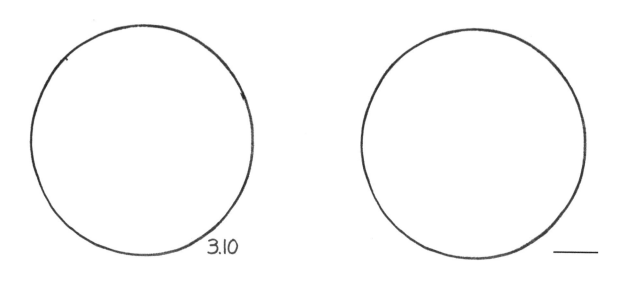

3.10

Check for accuracy. If you know it, save these others for future review.

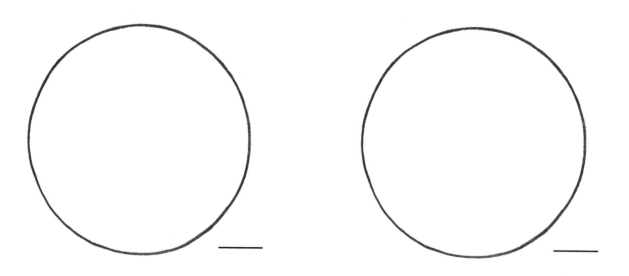

Acceleration: Practice drawing as quickly as possible.
Compare to original to ensure nothing was overlooked.

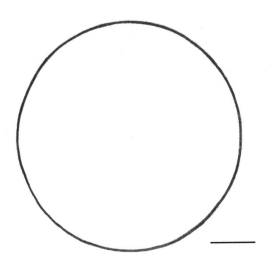 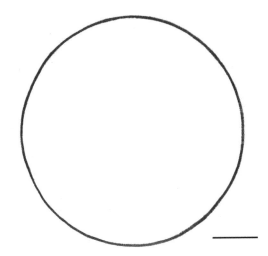

Time yourself. Be sure your drawing is complete within 15 seconds.
Jot down your time below. Be aware which drawings require more time.

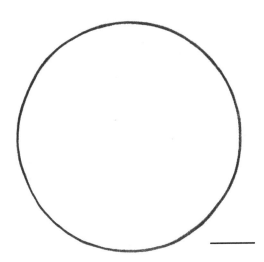 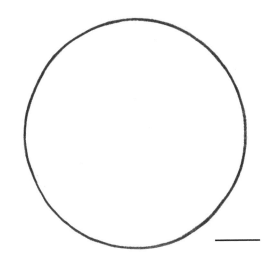

Time: _____   Time: _____

Orientation: Draw the icons you have learned in context. After your drawings are complete, express the meaning of each in sign language and then in spoken language.

3.10

4.0 RESPECT FOR CONSUMERS

Tenet: Interpreters demonstrate respect for consumers.

Illustrative Behavior - Interpreters:

4.1 Consider consumer requests or needs regarding language preferences, and render the message accordingly (interpreted or transliterated).

4.2 Approach consumers with a professional demeanor at all times.

4.3 Obtain the consent of consumers before bringing an intern to an assignment.

4.4 Facilitate communication access and equality, and support the full interaction and independence of consumers.

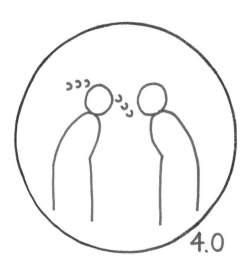

4.0 Tenet: Interpreters demonstrate respect for consumers.

Explanation:

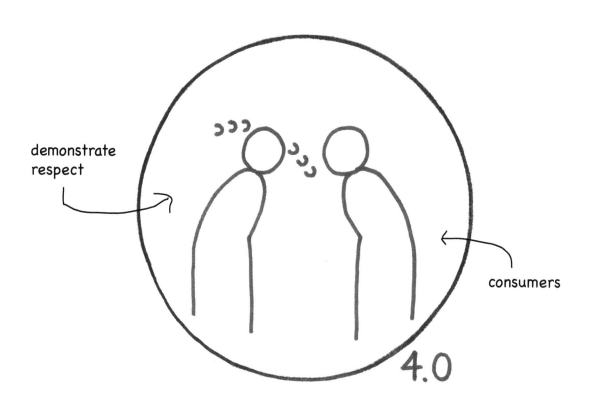

demonstrate respect

consumers

4.0

Imitation: Trace the image below.

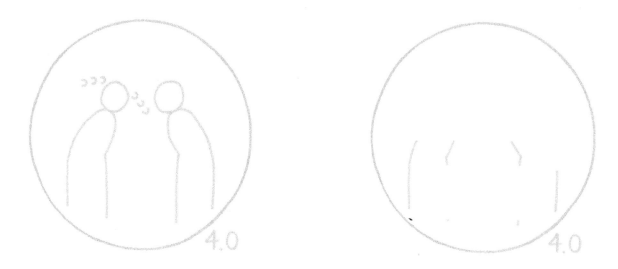

4.0

Comprehension:

Expression: Draw with understanding.

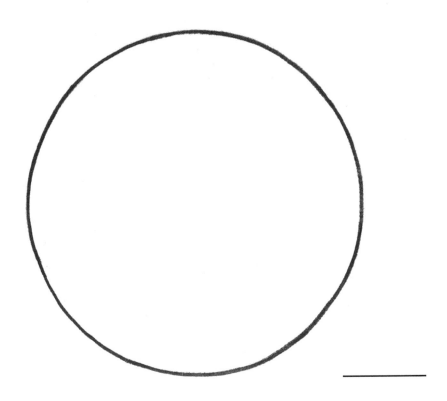

_____

Reflection: Make notes about the meaning.
Clarify your understanding or write down questions to address with a mentor.

_____

_____

_____

_____

_____

Memorization: Practice drawing without turning back to see the original.

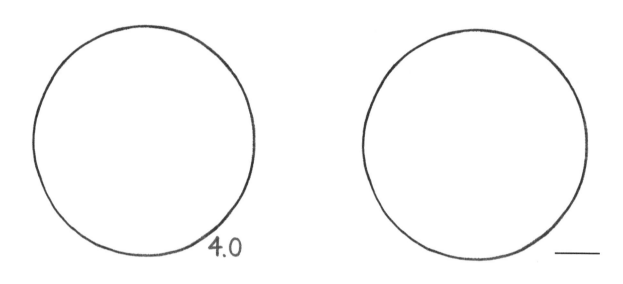

4.0

Check for accuracy. If you know it, save these others for future review.

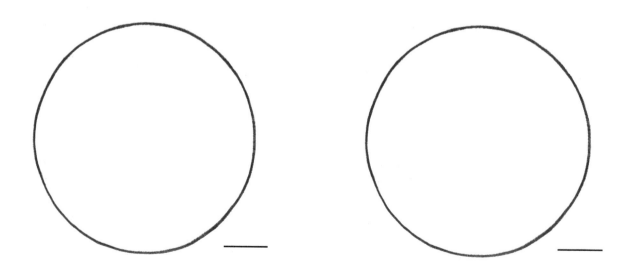

Acceleration: Practice drawing as quickly as possible.
Compare to original to ensure nothing was overlooked.

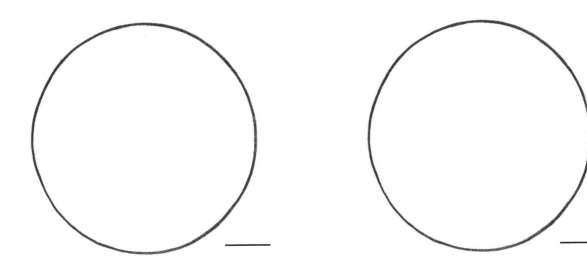

Time yourself. Be sure your drawing is complete within 15 seconds.
Jot down your time below. Be aware which drawings require more time.

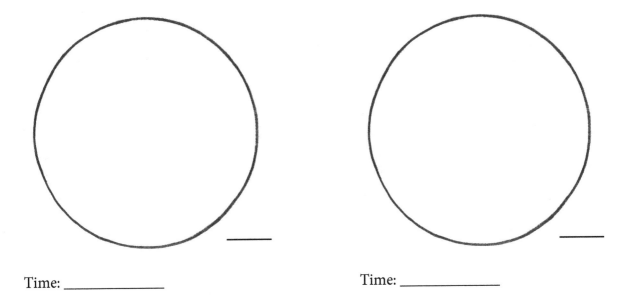

Time: _____   Time: _____

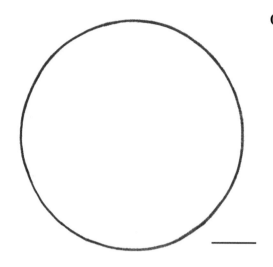

Orientation: Draw the icons you have learned in context. After your drawings are complete, express the meaning of each in sign language and then in spoken language.

4.1

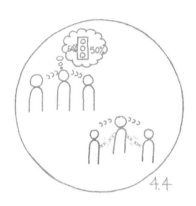

4.4

4.2

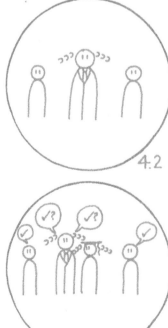

4.3

4.0

4.0 RESPECT FOR CONSUMERS

Tenet: Interpreters demonstrate respect for consumers.

Illustrative Behavior - Interpreters:

4.1 Consider consumer requests or needs regarding language preferences, and render the message accordingly (interpreted or transliterated).

4.2 Approach consumers with a professional demeanor at all times.

4.3 Obtain the consent of consumers before bringing an intern to an assignment.

4.4 Facilitate communication access and equality, and support the full interaction and independence of consumers.

4.1

4.1 Consider consumer requests or needs regarding language preferences, and render the message accordingly.

Explanation:

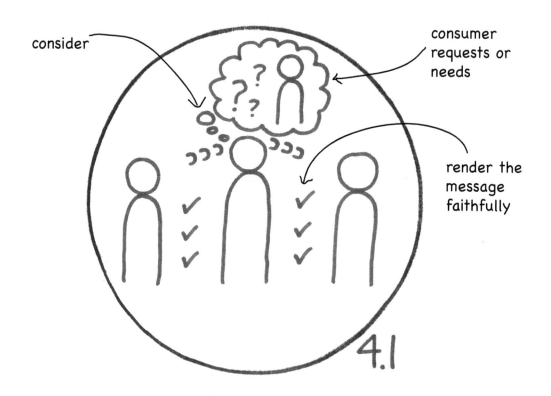

Imitation: Trace the image below.

Comprehension:

Expression: Draw with understanding.

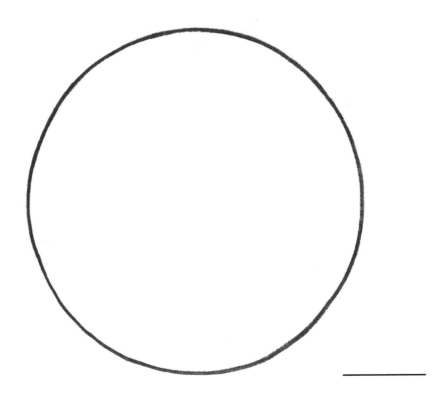

Reflection: Make notes about the meaning.

Clarify your understanding or write down questions to address with a mentor.

_____

_____

_____

_____

_____

Memorization: Practice drawing without turning back to see the original.

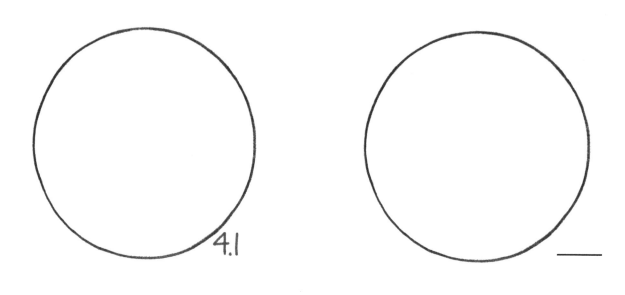

4.1

Check for accuracy. If you know it, save these others for future review.

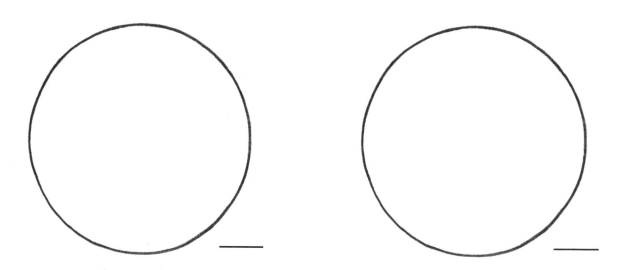

4.1

Acceleration: Practice drawing as quickly as possible.
Compare to original to ensure nothing was overlooked.

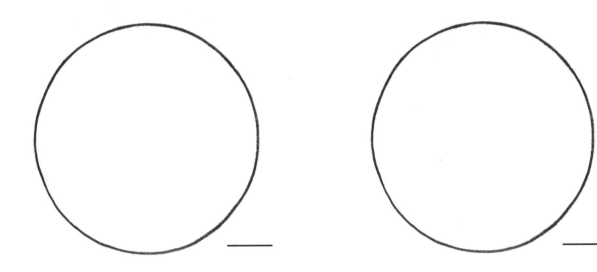

Time yourself. Be sure your drawing is complete within 15 seconds.
Jot down your time below. Be aware which drawings require more time.

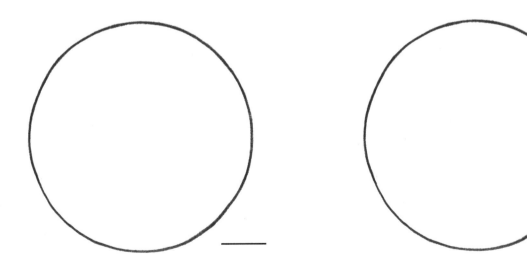

Time: _____   Time: _____

4.1

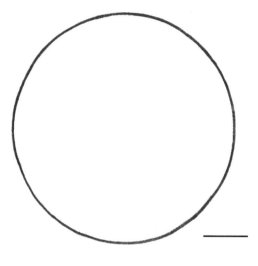

Orientation: Draw the icons you have learned in context. After your drawings are complete, express the meaning of each in sign language and then in spoken language.

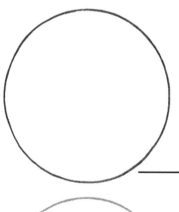

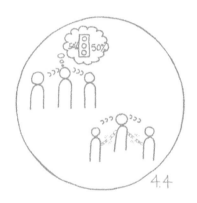

4.4

4.2

4.3

4.1

4.0 RESPECT FOR CONSUMERS

Tenet: Interpreters demonstrate respect for consumers.

Illustrative Behavior - Interpreters:

4.1 Consider consumer requests or needs regarding language preferences, and render the message accordingly (interpreted or transliterated).

4.2 Approach consumers with a professional demeanor at all times.

4.3 Obtain the consent of consumers before bringing an intern to an assignment.

4.4 Facilitate communication access and equality, and support the full interaction and independence of consumers.

4.2 Approach consumers with a professional demeanor at all times.

Explanation:

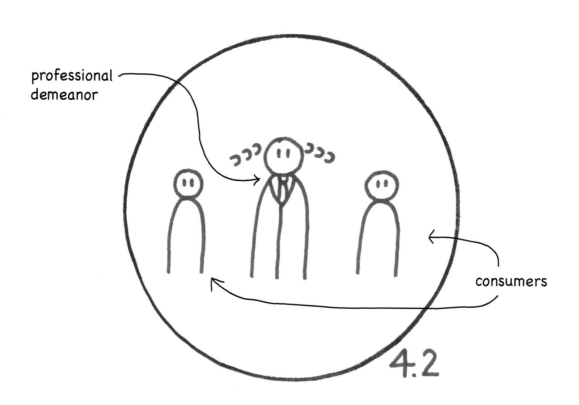

Imitation: Trace the image below.

Comprehension:

Expression: Draw with understanding.

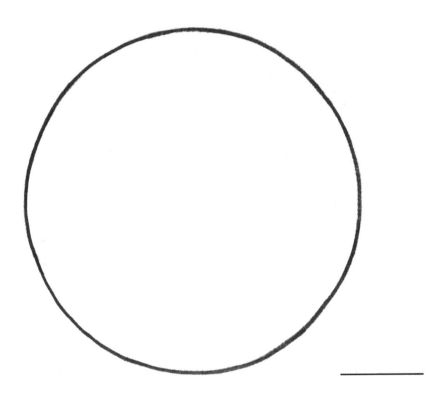

Reflection: Make notes about the meaning.
Clarify your understanding or write down questions to address with a mentor.

_____

_____

_____

_____

_____

4.2

Memorization: Practice drawing without turning back to see the original.

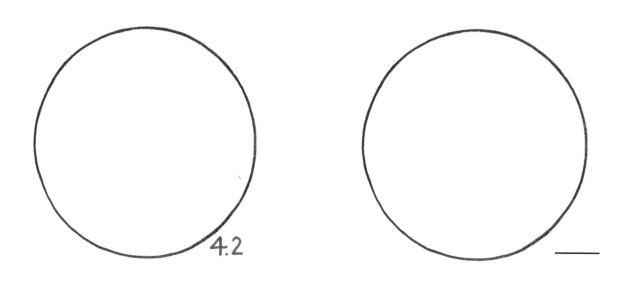

4.2

Check for accuracy. If you know it, save these others for future review.

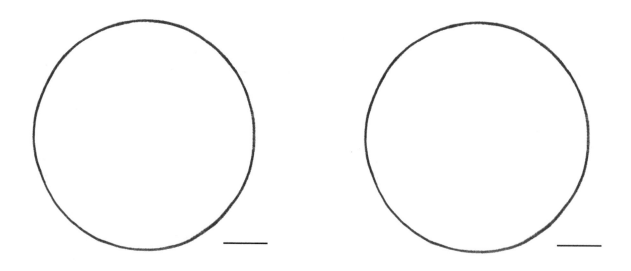

Acceleration: Practice drawing as quickly as possible.
Compare to original to ensure nothing was overlooked.

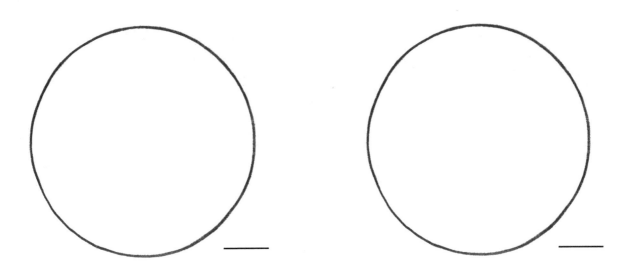

Time yourself. Be sure your drawing is complete within 15 seconds.
Jot down your time below. Be aware which drawings require more time.

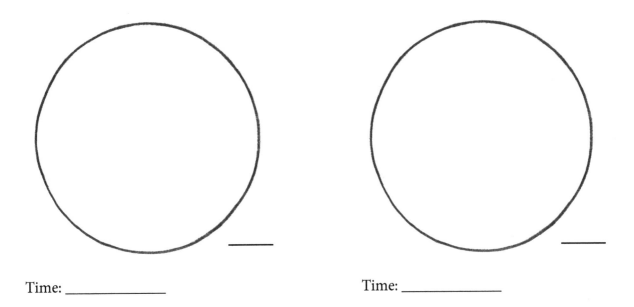

Time: _____   Time: _____

4.2

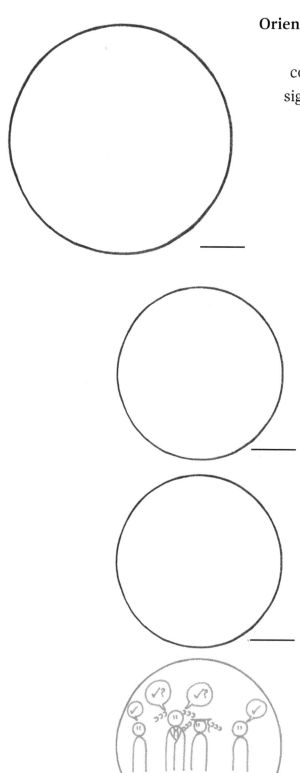

Orientation: Draw the icons you have learned in context. After your drawings are complete, express the meaning of each in sign language and then in spoken language.

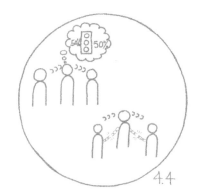

4.4

4.3

4.2

4.0 RESPECT FOR CONSUMERS

Tenet: Interpreters demonstrate respect for consumers.

Illustrative Behavior - Interpreters:

4.1 Consider consumer requests or needs regarding language preferences, and render the message accordingly (interpreted or transliterated).

4.2 Approach consumers with a professional demeanor at all times.

4.3 Obtain the consent of consumers before bringing an intern to an assignment.

4.4 Facilitate communication access and equality, and support the full interaction and independence of consumers.

4.3

4.3 Obtain the consent of consumers before bringing an intern to an assignment.

Explanation:

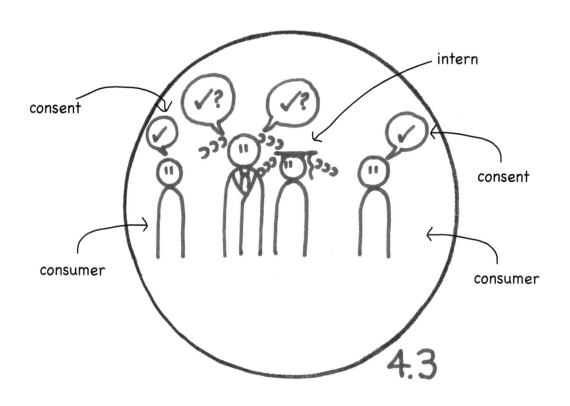

Imitation: Trace the image below.

Comprehension:

Expression: Draw with understanding.

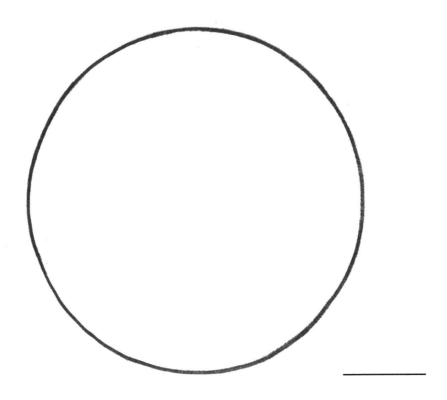

_____

Reflection: Make notes about the meaning.
Clarify your understanding or write down questions to address with a mentor.

_____

_____

_____

_____

_____

4.3

Memorization: Practice drawing without turning back to see the original.

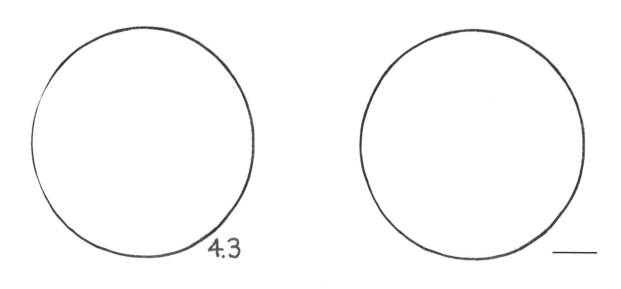

4.3

Check for accuracy. If you know it, save these others for future review.

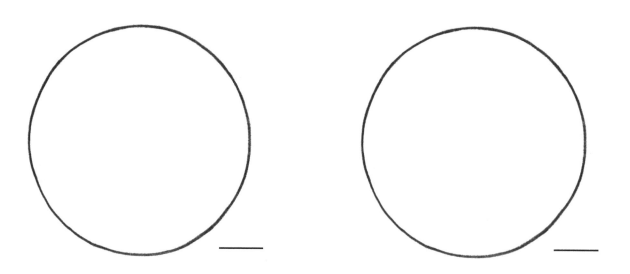

Acceleration: Practice drawing as quickly as possible.
Compare to original to ensure nothing was overlooked.

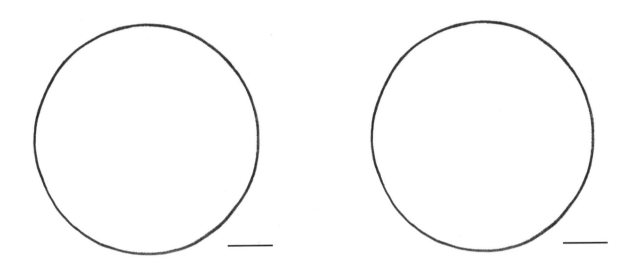

Time yourself. Be sure your drawing is complete within 15 seconds.
Jot down your time below. Be aware which drawings require more time.

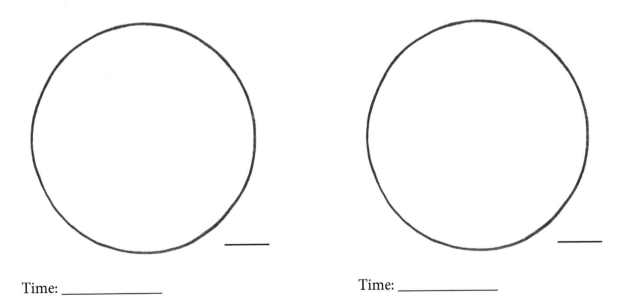

Time: _____   Time: _____

4.3

Orientation: Draw the icons you have learned in context. After your drawings are complete, express the meaning of each in sign language and then in spoken language.

4.4

4.0 RESPECT FOR CONSUMERS

Tenet: Interpreters demonstrate respect for consumers.

Illustrative Behavior - Interpreters:

4.1 Consider consumer requests or needs regarding language preferences, and render the message accordingly (interpreted or transliterated).

4.2 Approach consumers with a professional demeanor at all times.

4.3 Obtain the consent of consumers before bringing an intern to an assignment.

4.4 Facilitate communication access and equality, and support the full interaction and independence of consumers.

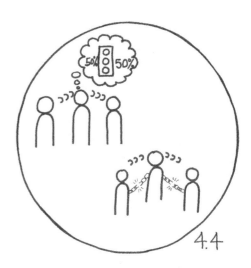

4.4

4.4 Facilitate communication access and equality,
and support the full interaction and independence of consumers.

Explanation:

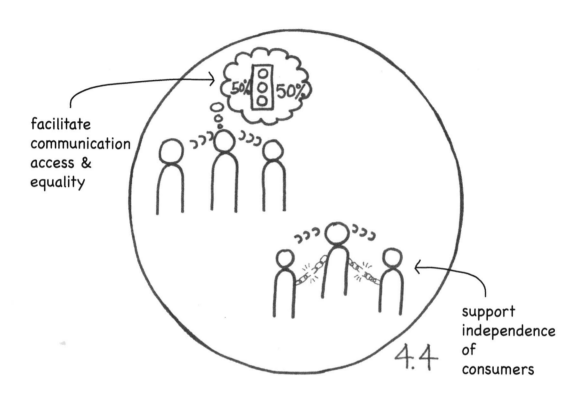

facilitate communication access & equality

support independence of consumers

4.4

Imitation: Trace the image below.

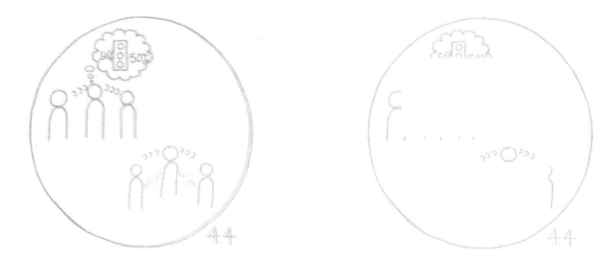

4.4

Comprehension:

Expression: Draw with understanding.

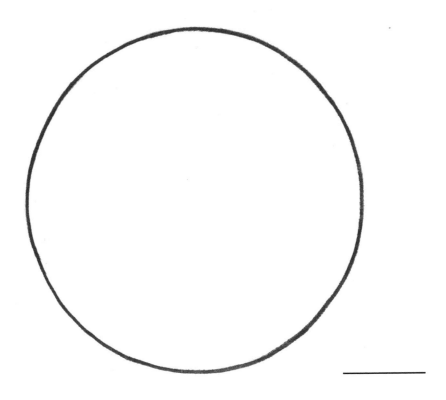

Reflection: Make notes about the meaning.

Clarify your understanding or write down questions to address with a mentor.

_____

_____

_____

_____

_____

Memorization: Practice drawing without turning back to see the original.

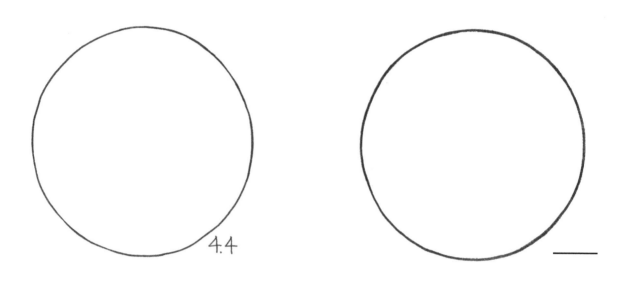

4.4

Check for accuracy. If you know it, save these others for future review.

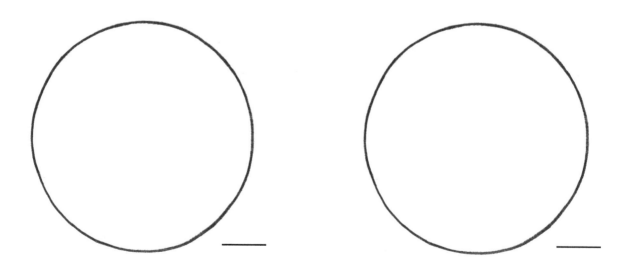

Acceleration: Practice drawing as quickly as possible.
Compare to original to ensure nothing was overlooked.

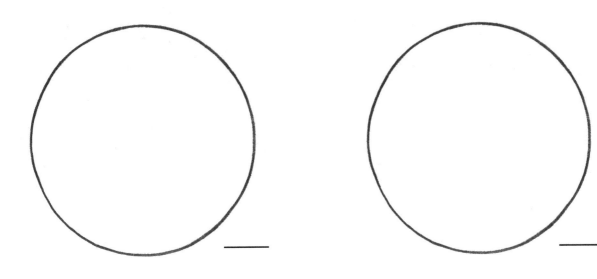

Time yourself. Be sure your drawing is complete within 15 seconds.
Jot down your time below. Be aware which drawings require more time.

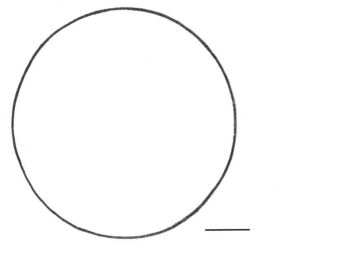

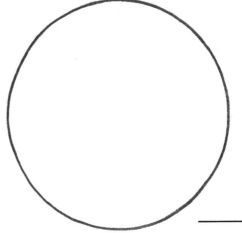

Time: _____

Time: _____

4.4

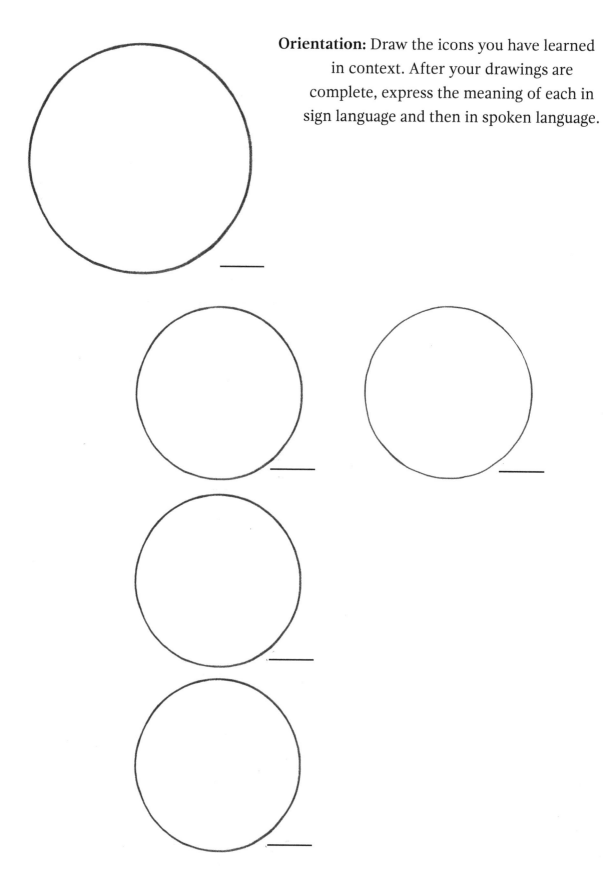

Orientation: Draw the icons you have learned in context. After your drawings are complete, express the meaning of each in sign language and then in spoken language.

4.4

5.0 RESPECT FOR COLLEAGUES

Tenet: Interpreters demonstrate respect for colleagues, interns and students of the profession.

Illustrative Behavior - Interpreters:

5.1 Maintain civility toward colleagues, interns, and students.

5.2 Work cooperatively with team members through consultation before assignments regarding logistics, providing professional and courteous assistance when asked and monitoring the accuracy of the message while functioning in the role of the support interpreter.

5.3 Approach colleagues privately to discuss and resolve breaches of ethical or professional conduct through standard conflict resolution methods; file a formal grievance only after such attempts have been unsuccessful or the breaches are harmful or habitual.

5.4 Assist and encourage colleagues by sharing information and serving as mentors when appropriate.

5.5 Obtain the consent of colleagues before bringing an intern to an assignment.

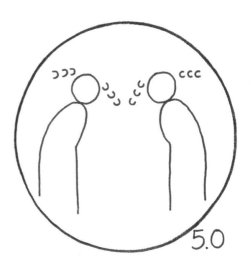

5.0 Tenet: Interpreters demonstrate respect for colleagues, interns and students of the profession.

Explanation:

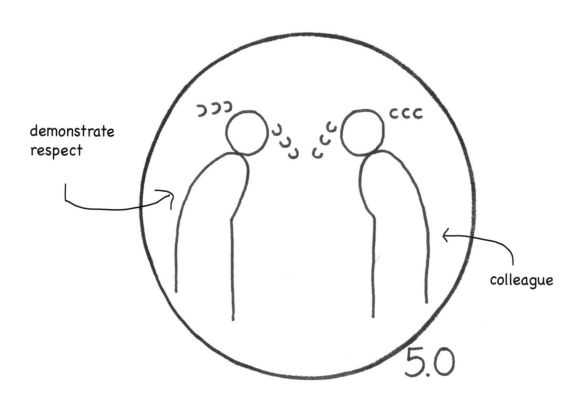

demonstrate respect

colleague

5.0

Imitation: Trace the image below.

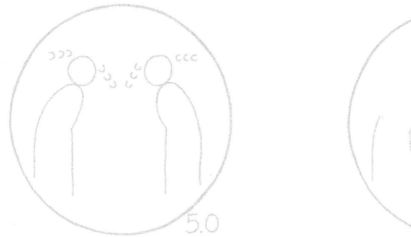

5.0

Comprehension:

Expression: Draw with understanding.

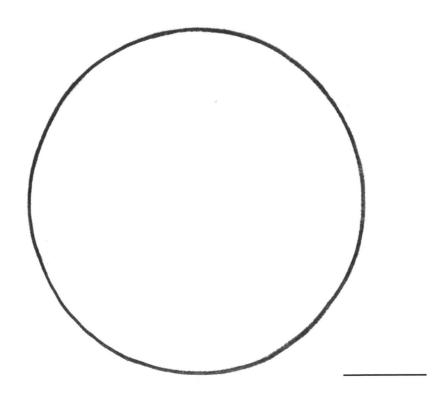

Reflection: Make notes about the meaning.
Clarify your understanding or write down questions to address with a mentor.

_____

_____

_____

_____

_____

Memorization: Practice drawing without turning back to see the original.

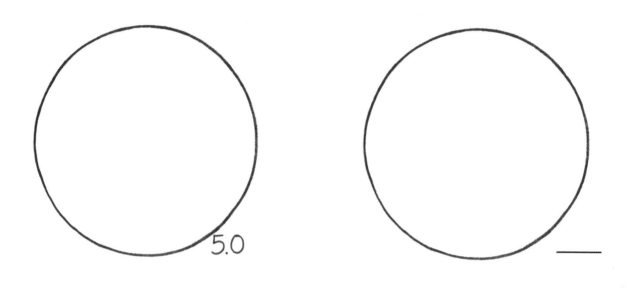

5.0

Check for accuracy. If you know it, save these others for future review.

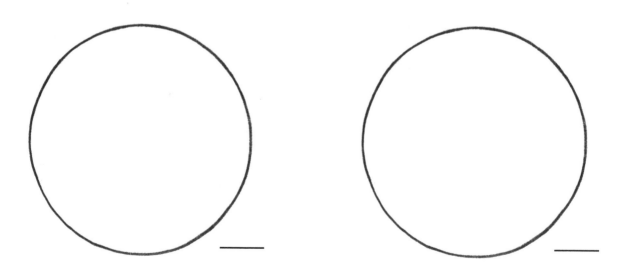

Acceleration: Practice drawing as quickly as possible.
Compare to original to ensure nothing was overlooked.

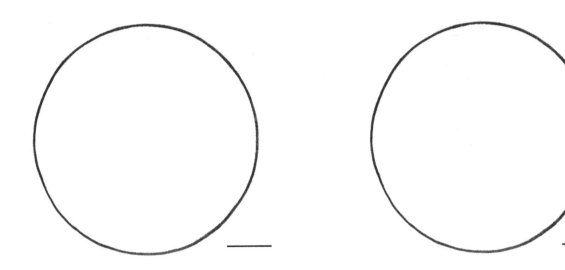

Time yourself. Be sure your drawing is complete within 15 seconds.
Jot down your time below. Be aware which drawings require more time.

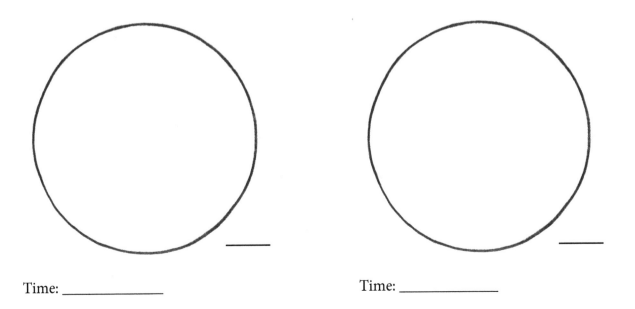

Time: _____   Time: _____

5.0

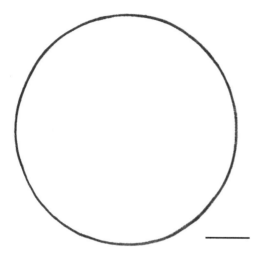

Orientation: Draw the icons you have learned in context. After your drawings are complete, express the meaning of each in sign language and then in spoken language.

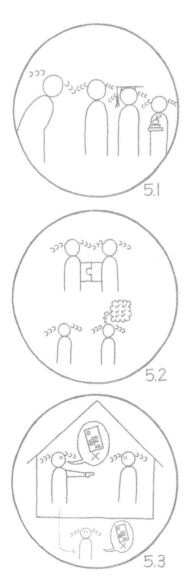

5.1

5.2

5.3

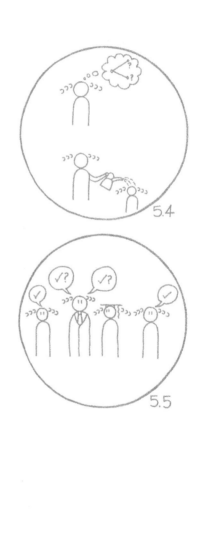

5.4

5.5

5.0

5.0 RESPECT FOR COLLEAGUES

Tenet: Interpreters demonstrate respect for colleagues, interns and students of the profession.

Illustrative Behavior - Interpreters:

5.1 Maintain civility toward colleagues, interns, and students.

5.2 Work cooperatively with team members through consultation before assignments regarding logistics, providing professional and courteous assistance when asked and monitoring the accuracy of the message while functioning in the role of the support interpreter.

5.3 Approach colleagues privately to discuss and resolve breaches of ethical or professional conduct through standard conflict resolution methods; file a formal grievance only after such attempts have been unsuccessful or the breaches are harmful or habitual.

5.4 Assist and encourage colleagues by sharing information and serving as mentors when appropriate.

5.5 Obtain the consent of colleagues before bringing an intern to an assignment.

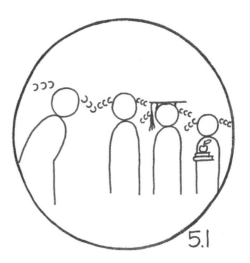
5.1

5.1 Maintain civility toward colleagues, interns, and students.

Explanation:

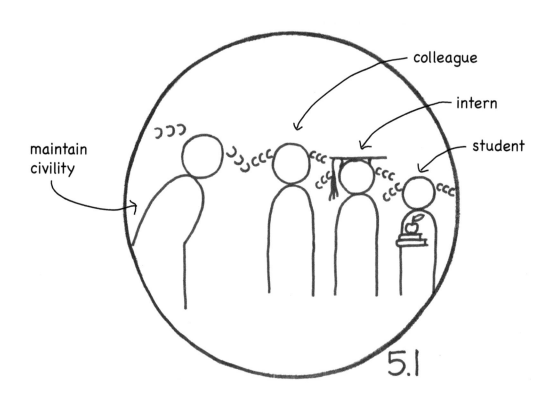

Imitation: Trace the image below.

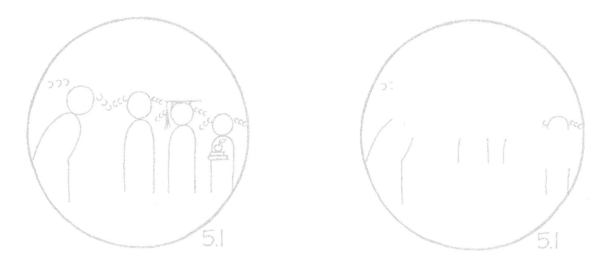

Comprehension:

Expression: Draw with understanding.

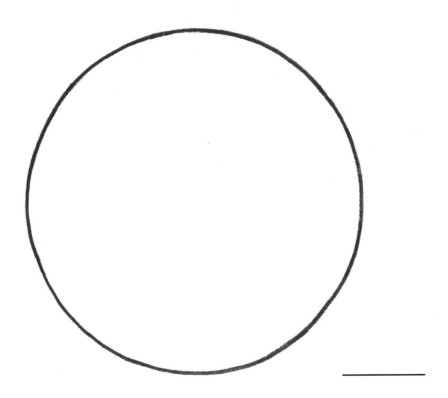

Reflection: Make notes about the meaning.
Clarify your understanding or write down questions to address with a mentor.

_____

_____

_____

_____

_____

Memorization: Practice drawing without turning back to see the original.

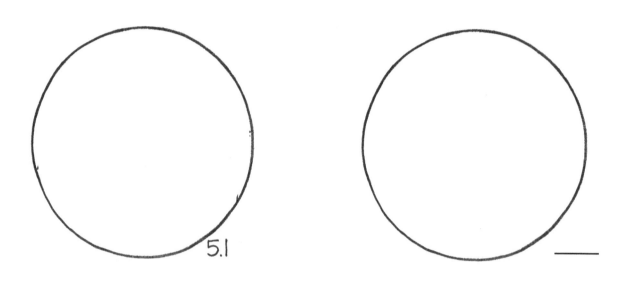

5.1

Check for accuracy. If you know it, save these others for future review.

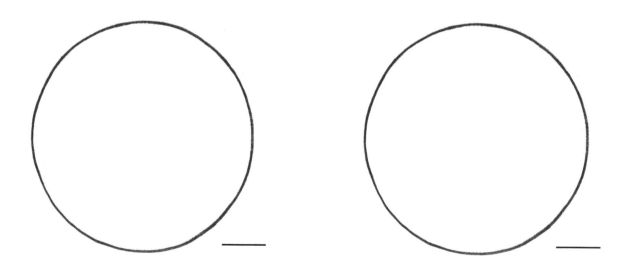

Acceleration: Practice drawing as quickly as possible.
Compare to original to ensure nothing was overlooked.

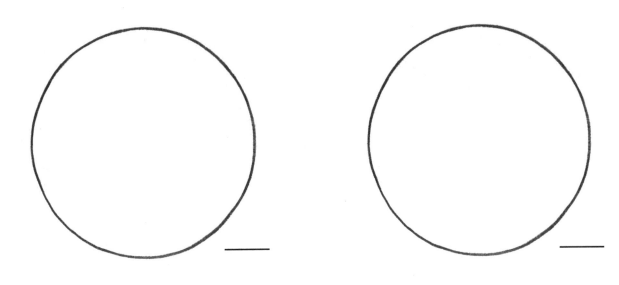

Time yourself. Be sure your drawing is complete within 15 seconds.
Jot down your time below. Be aware which drawings require more time.

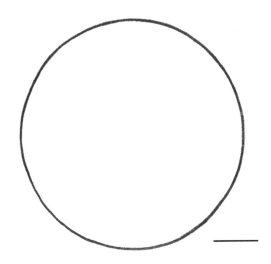

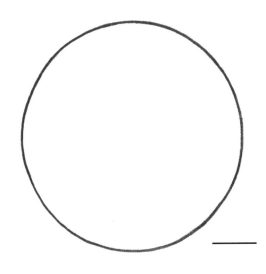

Time: _____

Time: _____

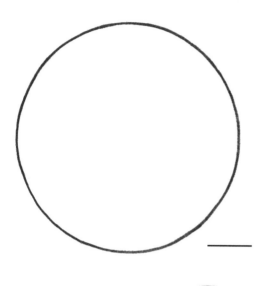

Orientation: Draw the icons you have learned in context. After your drawings are complete, express the meaning of each in sign language and then in spoken language.

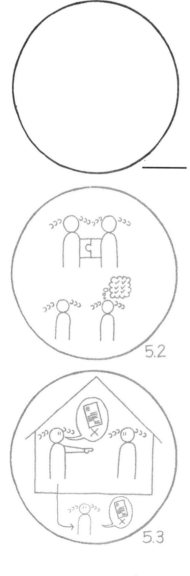

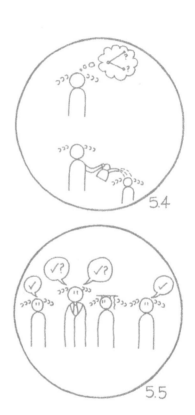

5.2

5.3

5.4

5.5

5.1

5.0 RESPECT FOR COLLEAGUES

Tenet: Interpreters demonstrate respect for colleagues, interns and students of the profession.

Illustrative Behavior - Interpreters:

5.1 Maintain civility toward colleagues, interns, and students.

5.2 Work cooperatively with team members through consultation before assignments regarding logistics, providing professional and courteous assistance when asked and monitoring the accuracy of the message while functioning in the role of the support interpreter.

5.3 Approach colleagues privately to discuss and resolve breaches of ethical or professional conduct through standard conflict resolution methods; file a formal grievance only after such attempts have been unsuccessful or the breaches are harmful or habitual.

5.4 Assist and encourage colleagues by sharing information and serving as mentors when appropriate.

5.5 Obtain the consent of colleagues before bringing an intern to an assignment.

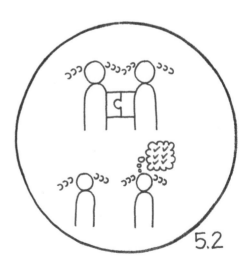

5.2

5.2 Work cooperatively with team members, providing professional and courteous assistance when asked and monitoring the accuracy of the message while functioning in the role of the support interpreter.

Explanation:

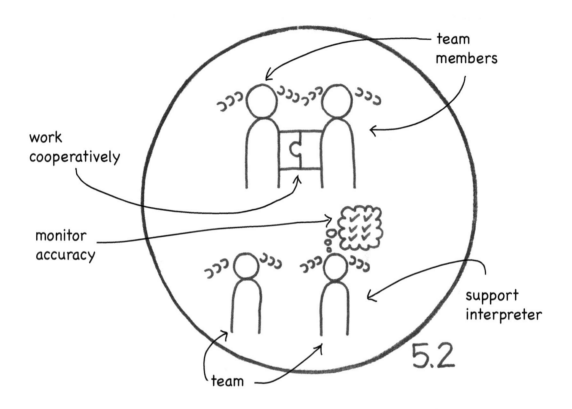

Imitation: Trace the image below.

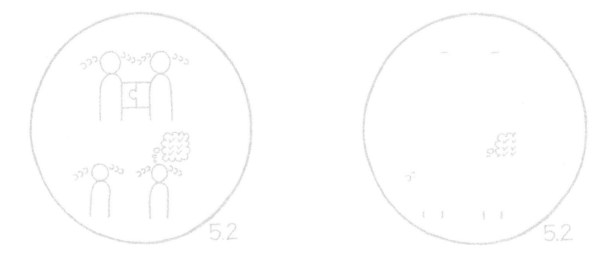

Comprehension:

Expression: Draw with understanding.

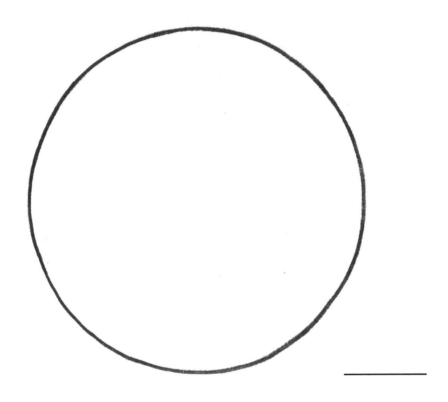
_____

Reflection: Make notes about the meaning.
Clarify your understanding or write down questions to address with a mentor.

_____

_____

_____

_____

_____

Memorization: Practice drawing without turning back to see the original.

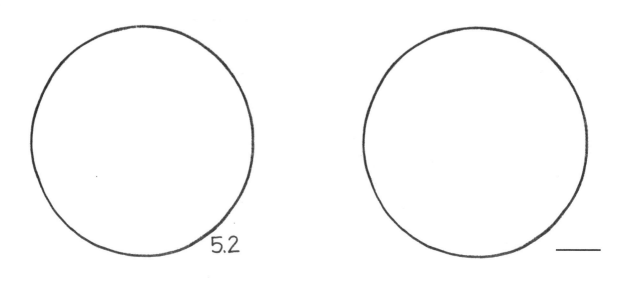

5.2

Check for accuracy. If you know it, save these others for future review.

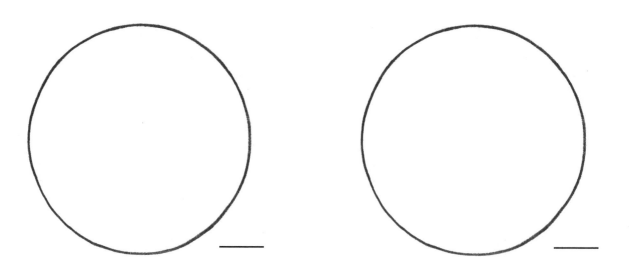

Acceleration: Practice drawing as quickly as possible.
Compare to original to ensure nothing was overlooked.

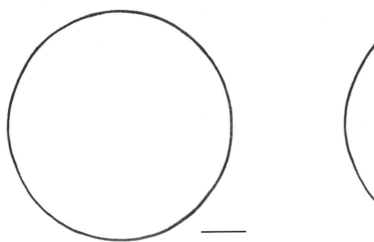

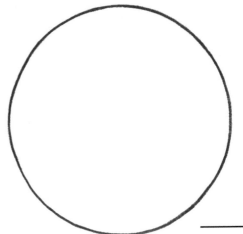

Time yourself. Be sure your drawing is complete within 15 seconds.
Jot down your time below. Be aware which drawings require more time.

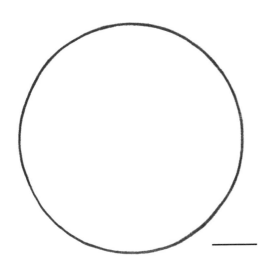

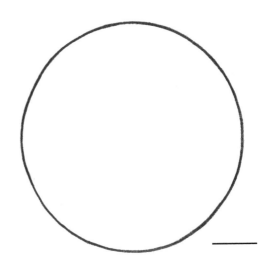

Time: _____

Time: _____

Orientation: Draw the icons you have learned in context. After your drawings are complete, express the meaning of each in sign language and then in spoken language.

5.2

5.0 RESPECT FOR COLLEAGUES

Tenet: Interpreters demonstrate respect for colleagues, interns and students of the profession.

Illustrative Behavior - Interpreters:

5.1 Maintain civility toward colleagues, interns, and students.

5.2 Work cooperatively with team members through consultation before assignments regarding logistics, providing professional and courteous assistance when asked and monitoring the accuracy of the message while functioning in the role of the support interpreter.

5.3 **Approach colleagues privately to discuss and resolve breaches of ethical or professional conduct through standard conflict resolution methods; file a formal grievance only after such attempts have been unsuccessful or the breaches are harmful or habitual.**

5.4 Assist and encourage colleagues by sharing information and serving as mentors when appropriate.

5.5 Obtain the consent of colleagues before bringing an intern to an assignment.

5.3

5.3 Approach colleagues privately to discuss and resolve breaches of ethical or professional conduct; file a formal grievance only after such attempts have been unsuccessful or the breaches are harmful or habitual.

Explanation:

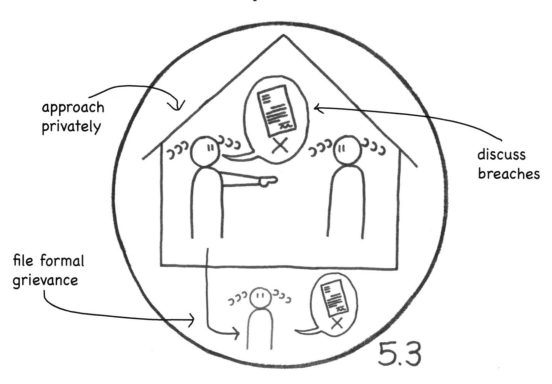

Imitation: Trace the image below.

Comprehension:

Expression: Draw with understanding.

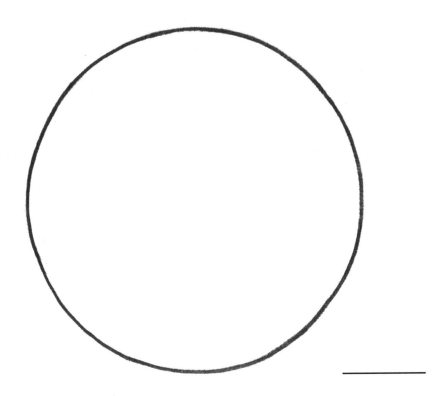

_____

Reflection: Make notes about the meaning.
Clarify your understanding or write down questions to address with a mentor.

_____

_____

_____

_____

_____

Memorization: Practice drawing without turning back to see the original.

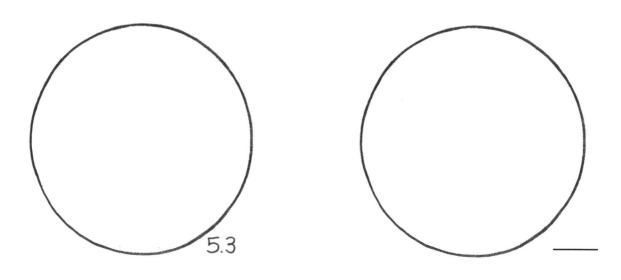

5.3

Check for accuracy. If you know it, save these others for future review.

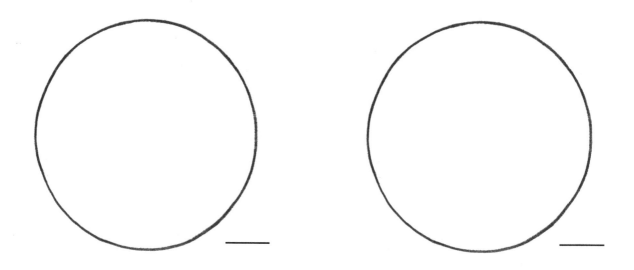

Acceleration: Practice drawing as quickly as possible.
Compare to original to ensure nothing was overlooked.

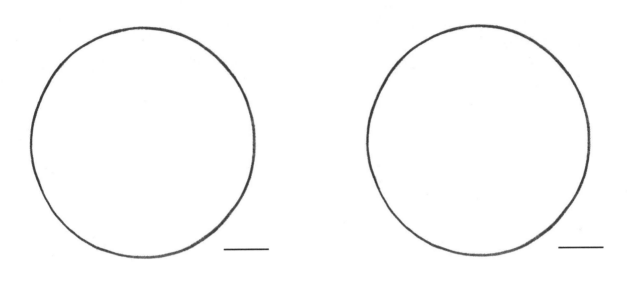

Time yourself. Be sure your drawing is complete within 15 seconds.
Jot down your time below. Be aware which drawings require more time.

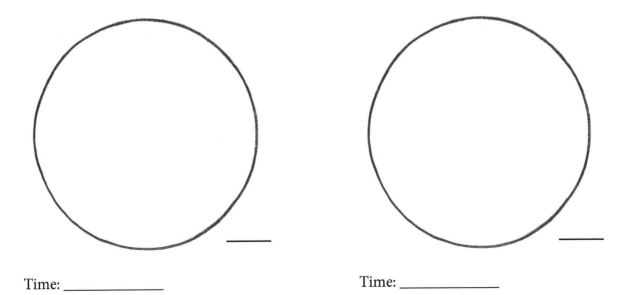

Time: _____   Time: _____

Orientation: Draw the icons you have learned in context. After your drawings are complete, express the meaning of each in sign language and then in spoken language.

5.4

5.5

5.3

5.0 RESPECT FOR COLLEAGUES

Tenet: Interpreters demonstrate respect for colleagues, interns and students of the profession.

Illustrative Behavior - Interpreters:

5.1 Maintain civility toward colleagues, interns, and students.

5.2 Work cooperatively with team members through consultation before assignments regarding logistics, providing professional and courteous assistance when asked and monitoring the accuracy of the message while functioning in the role of the support interpreter.

5.3 Approach colleagues privately to discuss and resolve breaches of ethical or professional conduct through standard conflict resolution methods; file a formal grievance only after such attempts have been unsuccessful or the breaches are harmful or habitual.

5.4 Assist and encourage colleagues by sharing information and serving as mentors when appropriate.

5.5 Obtain the consent of colleagues before bringing an intern to an assignment.

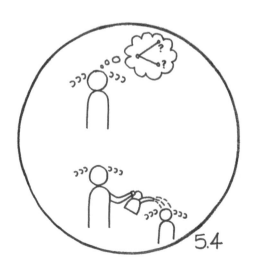

5.4

5.4 Assist and encourage colleagues by sharing information
and serving as mentors when appropriate.

Explanation:

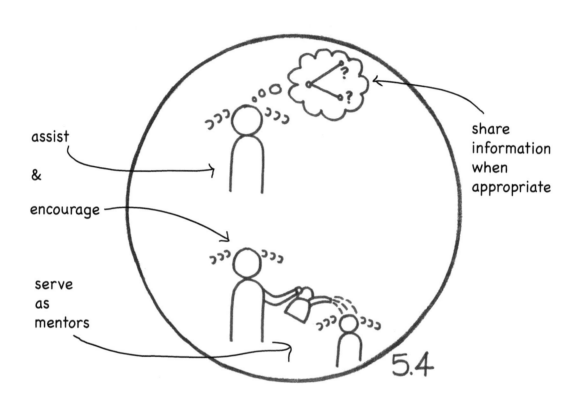

assist

&

encourage

serve
as
mentors

share
information
when
appropriate

5.4

Imitation: Trace the image below.

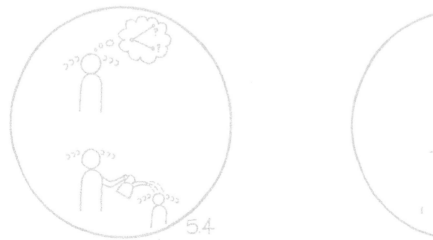

5.4

Comprehension:

Expression: Draw with understanding.

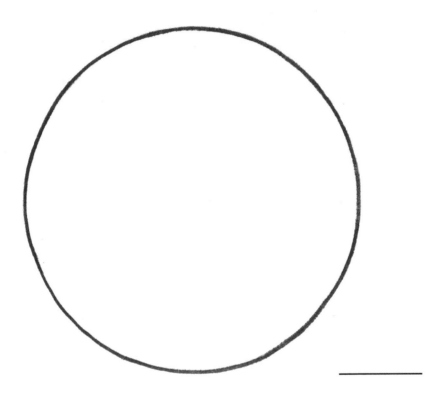

Reflection: Make notes about the meaning.

Clarify your understanding or write down questions to address with a mentor.

_____

_____

_____

_____

_____

Memorization: Practice drawing without turning back to see the original.

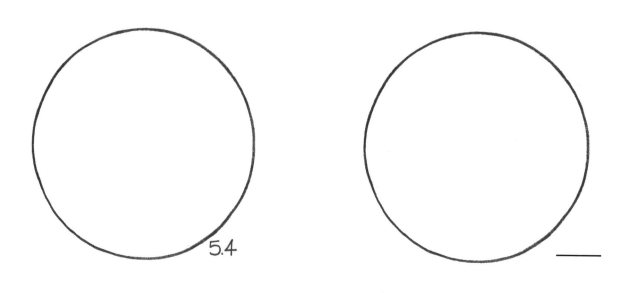

5.4

Check for accuracy. If you know it, save these others for future review.

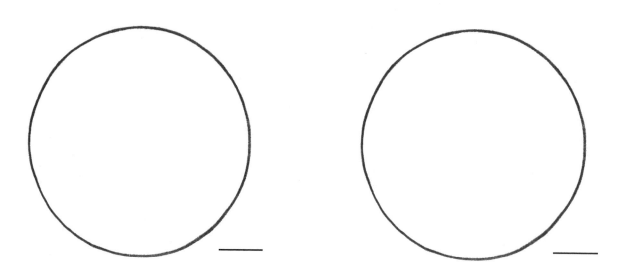

Acceleration: Practice drawing as quickly as possible.
Compare to original to ensure nothing was overlooked.

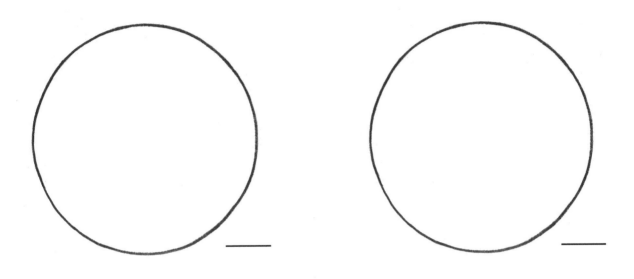

Time yourself. Be sure your drawing is complete within 15 seconds.
Jot down your time below. Be aware which drawings require more time.

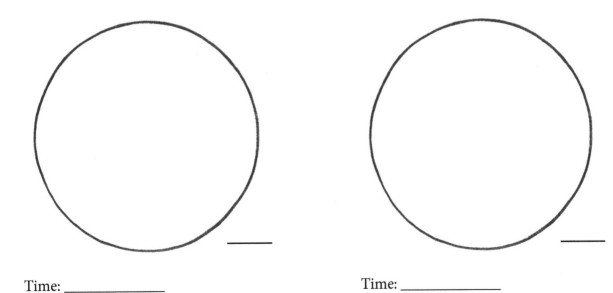

Time: _____   Time: _____

Orientation: Draw the icons you have learned in context. After your drawings are complete, express the meaning of each in sign language and then in spoken language.

5.5

5.4

5.0 RESPECT FOR COLLEAGUES

Tenet: Interpreters demonstrate respect for colleagues, interns and students of the profession.

Illustrative Behavior - Interpreters:

5.1 Maintain civility toward colleagues, interns, and students.

5.2 Work cooperatively with team members through consultation before assignments regarding logistics, providing professional and courteous assistance when asked and monitoring the accuracy of the message while functioning in the role of the support interpreter.

5.3 Approach colleagues privately to discuss and resolve breaches of ethical or professional conduct through standard conflict resolution methods; file a formal grievance only after such attempts have been unsuccessful or the breaches are harmful or habitual.

5.4 Assist and encourage colleagues by sharing information and serving as mentors when appropriate.

5.5 Obtain the consent of colleagues before bringing an intern to an assignment.

5.5 Obtain the consent of colleagues before bringing an intern to an assignment.

Explanation:

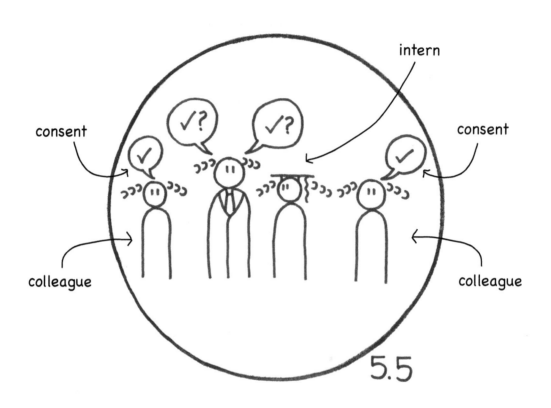

Imitation: Trace the image below.

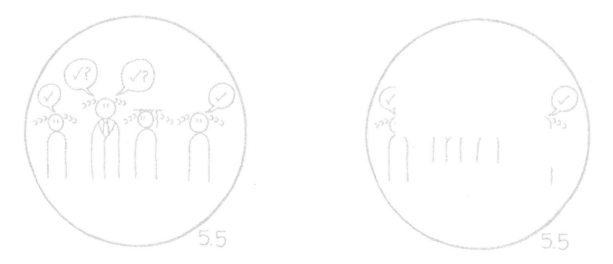

Comprehension:

Expression: Draw with understanding.

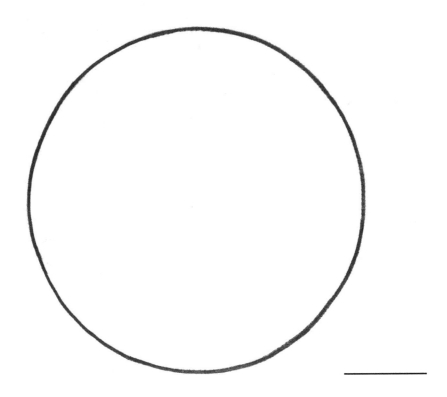

Reflection: Make notes about the meaning.
Clarify your understanding or write down questions to address with a mentor.

_____

_____

_____

_____

_____

Memorization: Practice drawing without turning back to see the original.

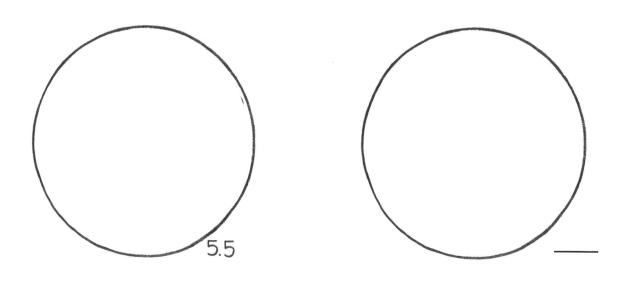

5.5

Check for accuracy. If you know it, save these others for future review.

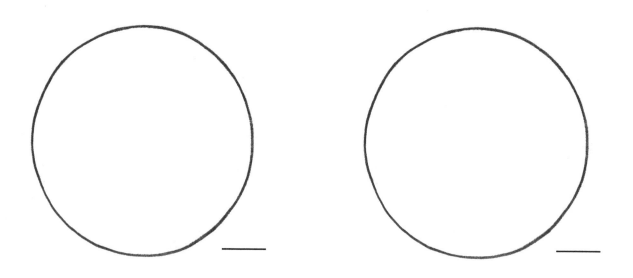

Acceleration: Practice drawing as quickly as possible.
Compare to original to ensure nothing was overlooked.

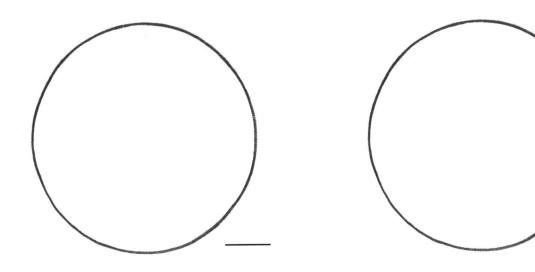

Time yourself. Be sure your drawing is complete within 15 seconds.
Jot down your time below. Be aware which drawings require more time.

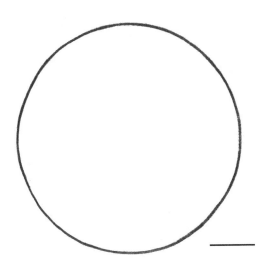
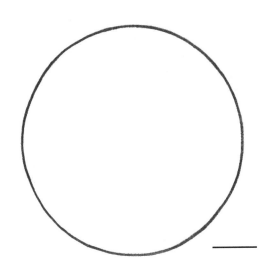

Time: _____   Time: _____

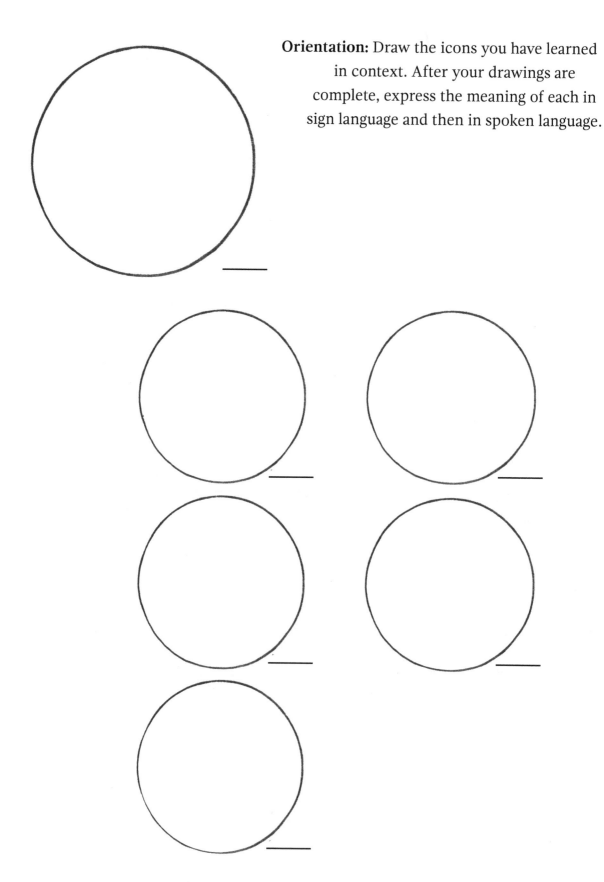

Orientation: Draw the icons you have learned in context. After your drawings are complete, express the meaning of each in sign language and then in spoken language.

5.5

6.0 BUSINESS PRACTICES

Tenet: Interpreters maintain ethical business practices.

Illustrative Behavior - Interpreters:

6.1 Accurately represent qualifications, such as certification, educational background, and experience, and provide documentation when requested.

6.2 Honor professional commitments and terminate assignments only when fair and justifiable grounds exist.

6.3 Promote conditions that are conducive to effective communication, inform the parties involved if such conditions do not exist, and seek appropriate remedies.

6.4 Inform appropriate parties in a timely manner when delayed or unable to fulfill assignments.

6.5 Reserve the option to decline or discontinue assignments if working conditions are not safe, healthy, or conducive to interpreting.

6.6 Refrain from harassment or coercion before, during, or after the provision of interpreting services.

6.7 Render pro bono services in a fair and reasonable manner.

6.8 Charge fair and reasonable fees for the performance of interpreting services and arrange for payment in a professional and judicious manner.

6.0

6.0 Tenet: Interpreters maintain ethical business practices.

Explanation:

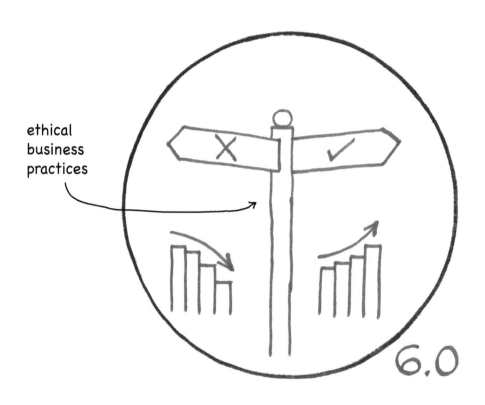

ethical business practices

6.0

Imitation: Trace the image below.

Comprehension:

Expression: Draw with understanding.

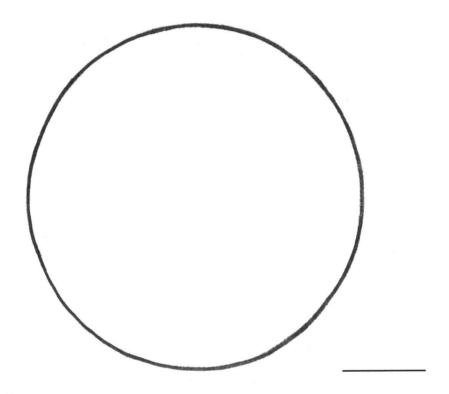

_____

Reflection: Make notes about the meaning.
Clarify your understanding or write down questions to address with a mentor.

_____

_____

_____

_____

_____

6.0

Memorization: Practice drawing without turning back to see the original.

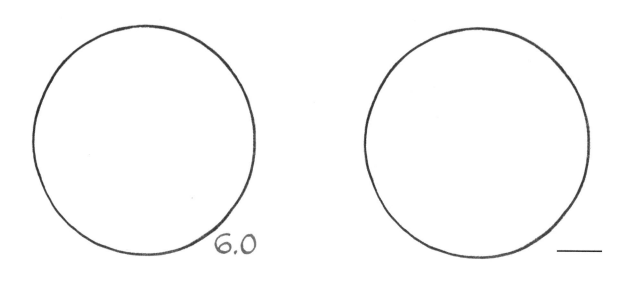

6.0

Check for accuracy. If you know it, save these others for future review.

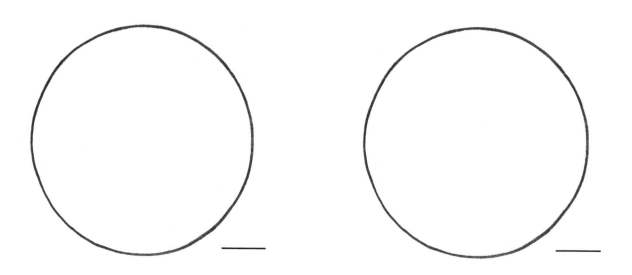

Acceleration: Practice drawing as quickly as possible.
Compare to original to ensure nothing was overlooked.

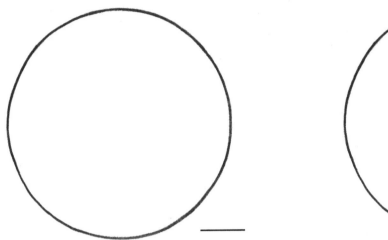
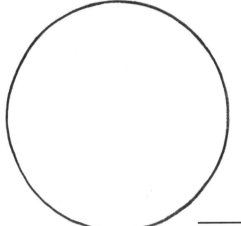

Time yourself. Be sure your drawing is complete within 15 seconds.
Jot down your time below. Be aware which drawings require more time.

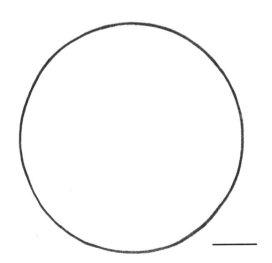
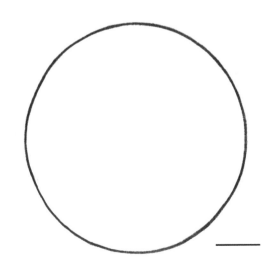

Time: _____   Time: _____

6.0

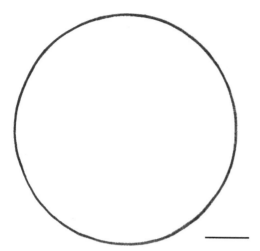

Orientation: Draw the icons you have learned in context. After your drawings are complete, express the meaning of each in sign language and then in spoken language.

6.0 BUSINESS PRACTICES

Tenet: Interpreters maintain ethical business practices.

Illustrative Behavior - Interpreters:

6.1 Accurately represent qualifications, such as certification, educational background, and experience, and provide documentation when requested.

6.2 Honor professional commitments and terminate assignments only when fair and justifiable grounds exist.

6.3 Promote conditions that are conducive to effective communication, inform the parties involved if such conditions do not exist, and seek appropriate remedies.

6.4 Inform appropriate parties in a timely manner when delayed or unable to fulfill assignments.

6.5 Reserve the option to decline or discontinue assignments if working conditions are not safe, healthy, or conducive to interpreting.

6.6 Refrain from harassment or coercion before, during, or after the provision of interpreting services.

6.7 Render pro bono services in a fair and reasonable manner.

6.8 Charge fair and reasonable fees for the performance of interpreting services and arrange for payment in a professional and judicious manner.

6.1

6.1 Accurately represent qualifications, such as certification, educational background, and experience, and provide documentation when requested.

Explanation:

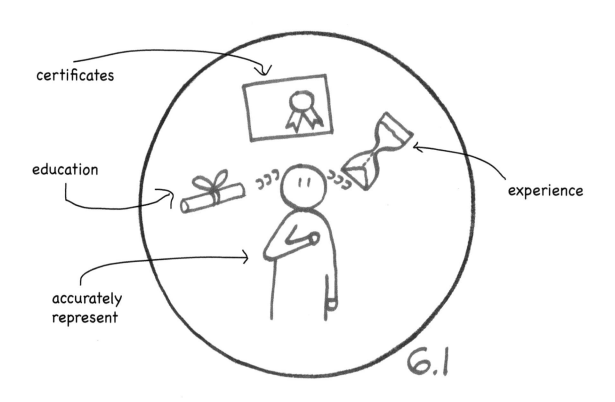

Imitation: Trace the image below.

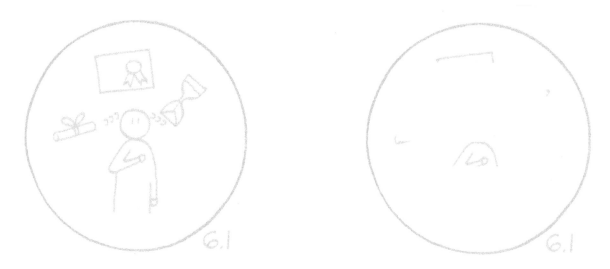

Comprehension:

Expression: Draw with understanding.

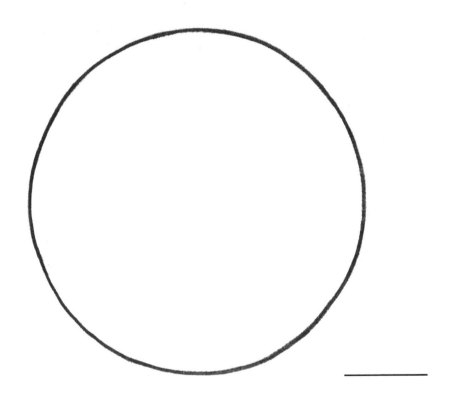

Reflection: Make notes about the meaning.
Clarify your understanding or write down questions to address with a mentor.

_____

_____

_____

_____

_____

Memorization: Practice drawing without turning back to see the original.

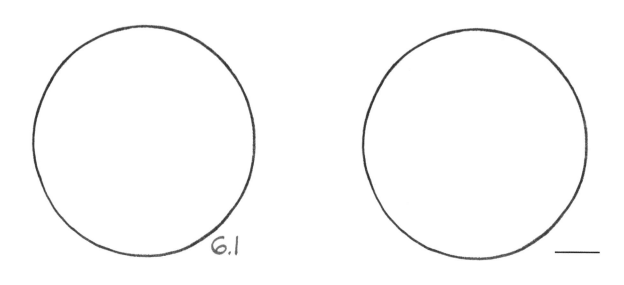

6.1

Check for accuracy. If you know it, save these others for future review.

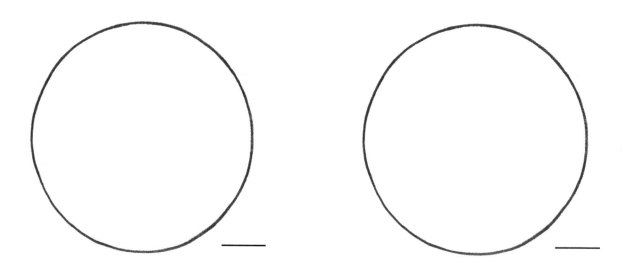

Acceleration: Practice drawing as quickly as possible.
Compare to original to ensure nothing was overlooked.

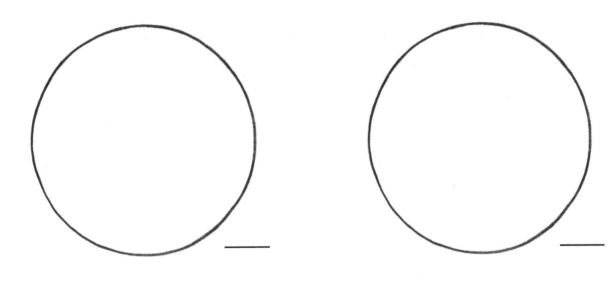

Time yourself. Be sure your drawing is complete within 15 seconds.
Jot down your time below. Be aware which drawings require more time.

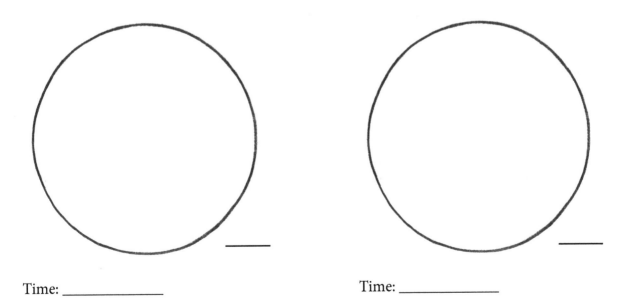

Time: _____   Time: _____

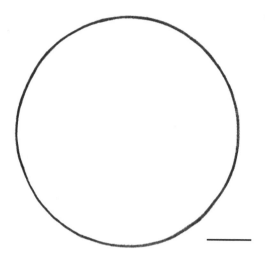

Orientation: Draw the icons you have learned in context. After your drawings are complete, express the meaning of each in sign language and then in spoken language.

6.0 BUSINESS PRACTICES

Tenet: Interpreters maintain ethical business practices.

Illustrative Behavior - Interpreters:

6.1 Accurately represent qualifications, such as certification, educational background, and experience, and provide documentation when requested.

6.2 Honor professional commitments and terminate assignments only when fair and justifiable grounds exist.

6.3 Promote conditions that are conducive to effective communication, inform the parties involved if such conditions do not exist, and seek appropriate remedies.

6.4 Inform appropriate parties in a timely manner when delayed or unable to fulfill assignments.

6.5 Reserve the option to decline or discontinue assignments if working conditions are not safe, healthy, or conducive to interpreting.

6.6 Refrain from harassment or coercion before, during, or after the provision of interpreting services.

6.7 Render pro bono services in a fair and reasonable manner.

6.8 Charge fair and reasonable fees for the performance of interpreting services and arrange for payment in a professional and judicious manner.

6.2 Honor professional commitments and terminate assignments only when fair and justifiable grounds exist.

Explanation:

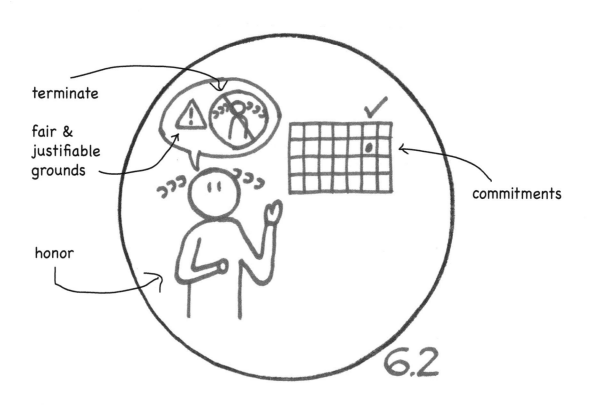

Imitation: Trace the image below.

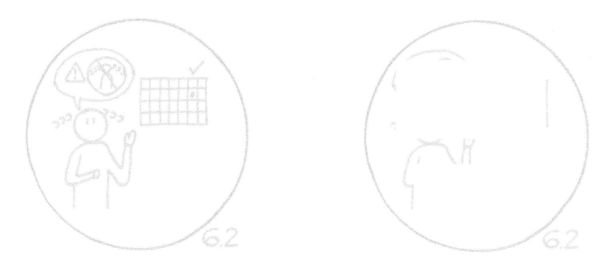

Comprehension:

Expression: Draw with understanding.

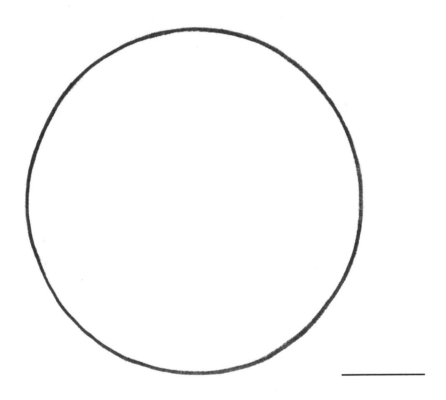

Reflection: Make notes about the meaning.
Clarify your understanding or write down questions to address with a mentor.

_____

_____

_____

_____

_____

Memorization: Practice drawing without turning back to see the original.

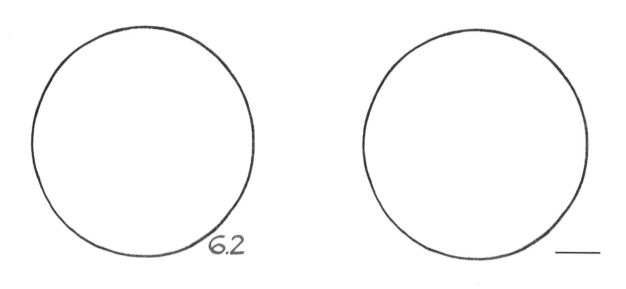

6.2

Check for accuracy. If you know it, save these others for future review.

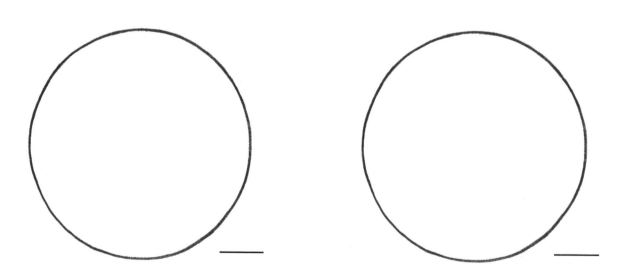

Acceleration: Practice drawing as quickly as possible.
Compare to original to ensure nothing was overlooked.

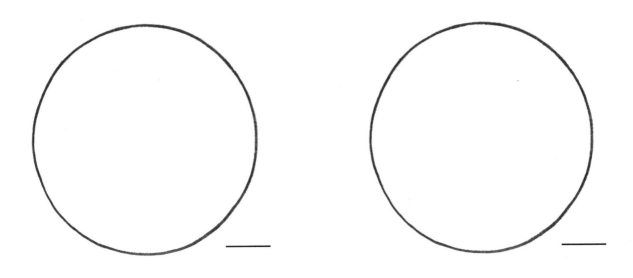

Time yourself. Be sure your drawing is complete within 15 seconds.
Jot down your time below. Be aware which drawings require more time.

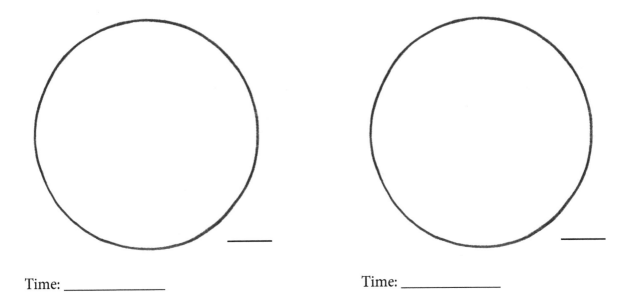

Time: _____

Time: _____

6.2

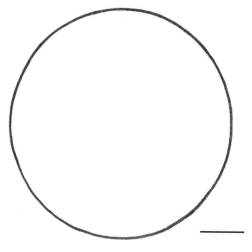

Orientation: Draw the icons you have learned in context. After your drawings are complete, express the meaning of each in sign language and then in spoken language.

6.2

6.0 BUSINESS PRACTICES

Tenet: Interpreters maintain ethical business practices.

Illustrative Behavior - Interpreters:

6.1 Accurately represent qualifications, such as certification, educational background, and experience, and provide documentation when requested.

6.2 Honor professional commitments and terminate assignments only when fair and justifiable grounds exist.

6.3 Promote conditions that are conducive to effective communication, inform the parties involved if such conditions do not exist, and seek appropriate remedies.

6.4 Inform appropriate parties in a timely manner when delayed or unable to fulfill assignments.

6.5 Reserve the option to decline or discontinue assignments if working conditions are not safe, healthy, or conducive to interpreting.

6.6 Refrain from harassment or coercion before, during, or after the provision of interpreting services.

6.7 Render pro bono services in a fair and reasonable manner.

6.8 Charge fair and reasonable fees for the performance of interpreting services and arrange for payment in a professional and judicious manner.

6.3

6.3 Promote conditions that are conducive to effective communication, inform the parties involved if such conditions do not exist, and seek appropriate remedies.

Explanation:

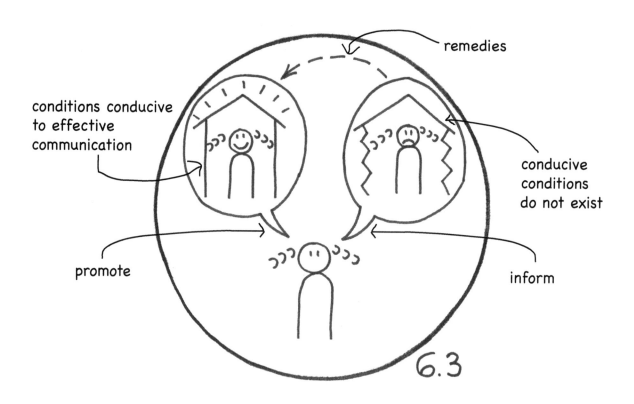

Imitation: Trace the image below.

Comprehension:

Expression: Draw with understanding.

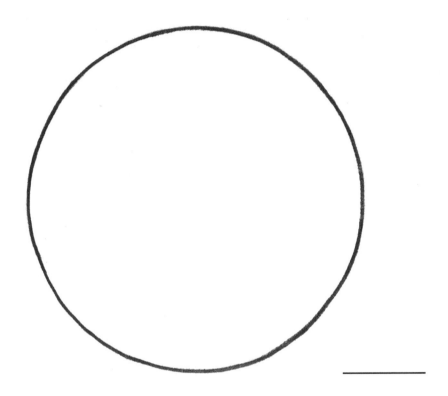

_____

Reflection: Make notes about the meaning.

Clarify your understanding or write down questions to address with a mentor.

_____

_____

_____

_____

_____

Memorization: Practice drawing without turning back to see the original.

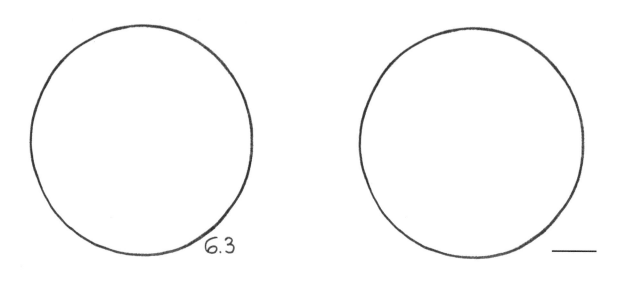

6.3

Check for accuracy. If you know it, save these others for future review.

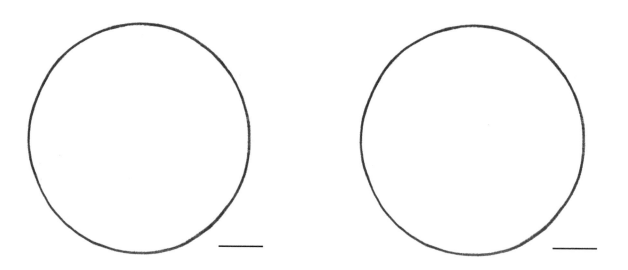

Acceleration: Practice drawing as quickly as possible.
Compare to original to ensure nothing was overlooked.

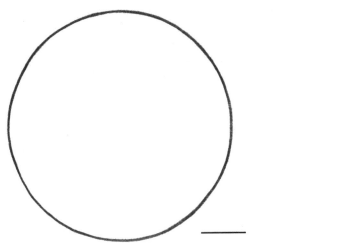

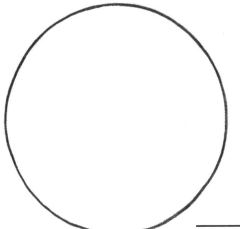

Time yourself. Be sure your drawing is complete within 15 seconds.
Jot down your time below. Be aware which drawings require more time.

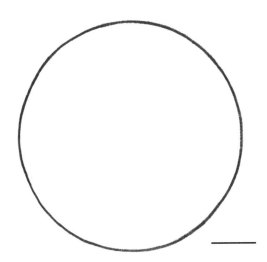

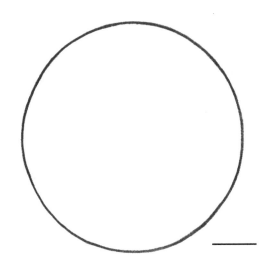

Time: _____

Time: _____

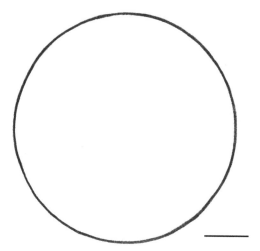

Orientation: Draw the icons you have learned in context. After your drawings are complete, express the meaning of each in sign language and then in spoken language.

6.4

6.7

6.5

6.8

6.6

6.3

6.0 BUSINESS PRACTICES

Tenet: Interpreters maintain ethical business practices.

Illustrative Behavior - Interpreters:

6.1 Accurately represent qualifications, such as certification, educational background, and experience, and provide documentation when requested.

6.2 Honor professional commitments and terminate assignments only when fair and justifiable grounds exist.

6.3 Promote conditions that are conducive to effective communication, inform the parties involved if such conditions do not exist, and seek appropriate remedies.

6.4 Inform appropriate parties in a timely manner when delayed or unable to fulfill assignments.

6.5 Reserve the option to decline or discontinue assignments if working conditions are not safe, healthy, or conducive to interpreting.

6.6 Refrain from harassment or coercion before, during, or after the provision of interpreting services.

6.7 Render pro bono services in a fair and reasonable manner.

6.8 Charge fair and reasonable fees for the performance of interpreting services and arrange for payment in a professional and judicious manner.

6.4

6.4 Inform appropriate parties in a timely manner when delayed or unable to fulfill assignments.

Explanation:

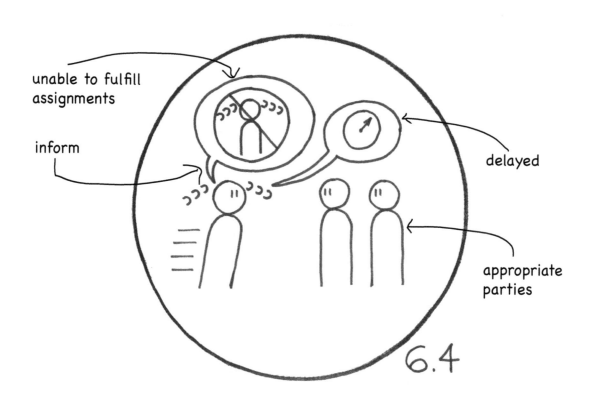

Imitation: Trace the image below.

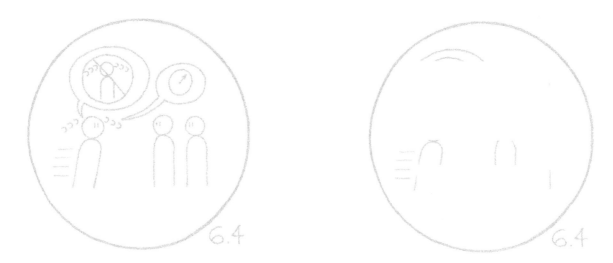

Comprehension:

Expression: Draw with understanding.

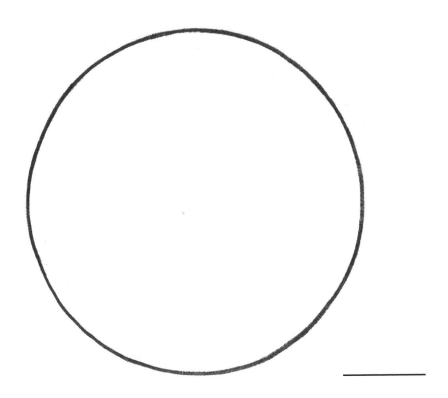

Reflection: Make notes about the meaning.
Clarify your understanding or write down questions to address with a mentor.

_____

_____

_____

_____

_____

Memorization: Practice drawing without turning back to see the original.

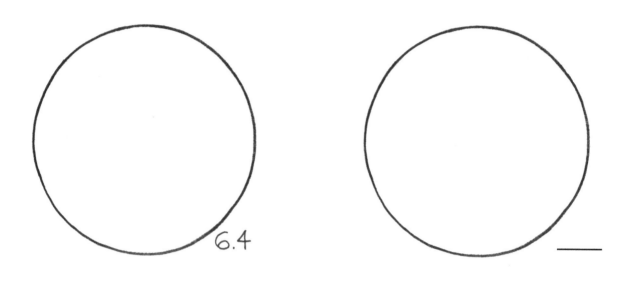

6.4

Check for accuracy. If you know it, save these others for future review.

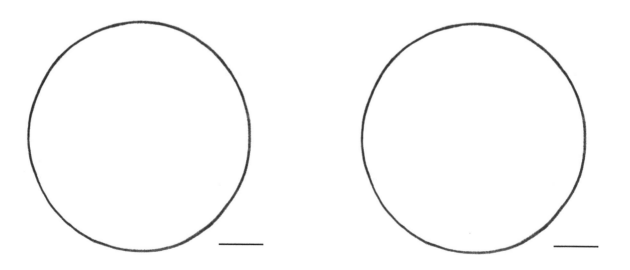

Acceleration: Practice drawing as quickly as possible.
Compare to original to ensure nothing was overlooked.

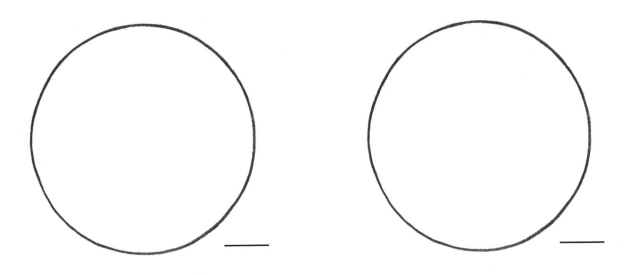

Time yourself. Be sure your drawing is complete within 15 seconds.
Jot down your time below. Be aware which drawings require more time.

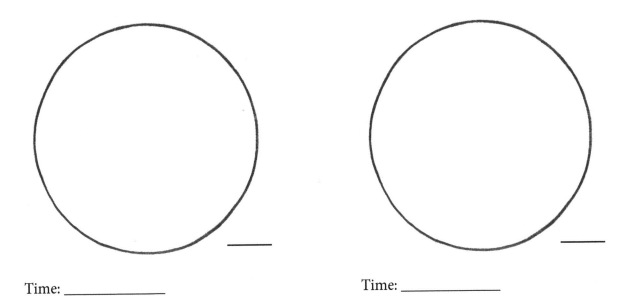

Time: _____

Time: _____

Orientation: Draw the icons you have learned in context. After your drawings are complete, express the meaning of each in sign language and then in spoken language.

6.4

6.0 BUSINESS PRACTICES

Tenet: Interpreters maintain ethical business practices.

Illustrative Behavior - Interpreters:

6.1 Accurately represent qualifications, such as certification, educational background, and experience, and provide documentation when requested.

6.2 Honor professional commitments and terminate assignments only when fair and justifiable grounds exist.

6.3 Promote conditions that are conducive to effective communication, inform the parties involved if such conditions do not exist, and seek appropriate remedies.

6.4 Inform appropriate parties in a timely manner when delayed or unable to fulfill assignments.

6.5 Reserve the option to decline or discontinue assignments if working conditions are not safe, healthy, or conducive to interpreting.

6.6 Refrain from harassment or coercion before, during, or after the provision of interpreting services.

6.7 Render pro bono services in a fair and reasonable manner.

6.8 Charge fair and reasonable fees for the performance of interpreting services and arrange for payment in a professional and judicious manner.

6.5

6.5 Reserve the option to decline or discontinue assignments
if working conditions are not safe, healthy, or conducive to interpreting.

Explanation:

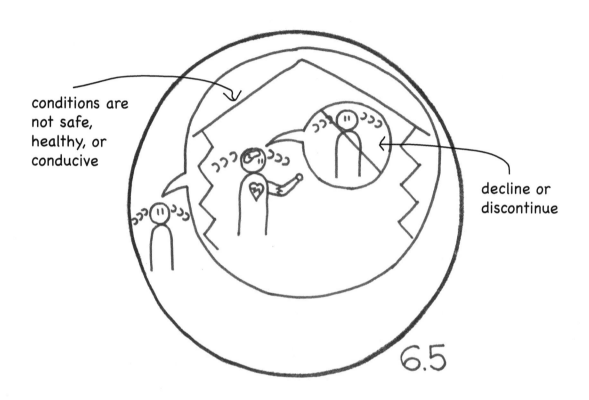

conditions are
not safe,
healthy, or
conducive

decline or
discontinue

6.5

Imitation: Trace the image below.

Comprehension:

Expression: Draw with understanding.

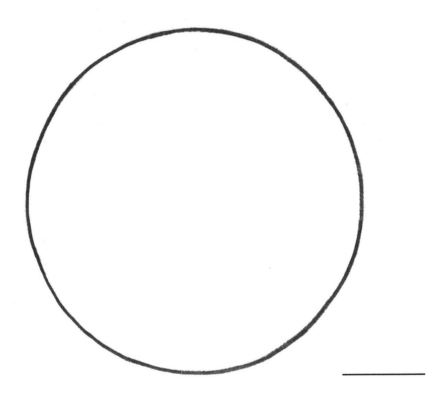

Reflection: Make notes about the meaning.
Clarify your understanding or write down questions to address with a mentor.

_____

_____

_____

_____

_____

Memorization: Practice drawing without turning back to see the original.

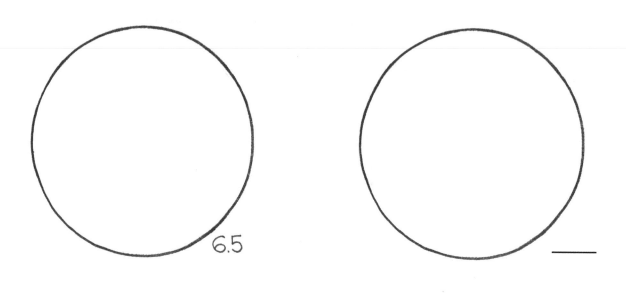

6.5

Check for accuracy. If you know it, save these others for future review.

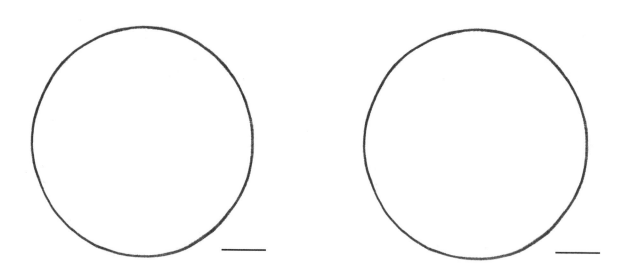

Acceleration: Practice drawing as quickly as possible.
Compare to original to ensure nothing was overlooked.

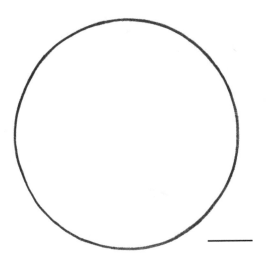 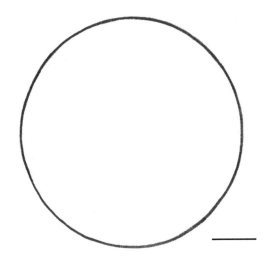

Time yourself. Be sure your drawing is complete within 15 seconds.
Jot down your time below. Be aware which drawings require more time.

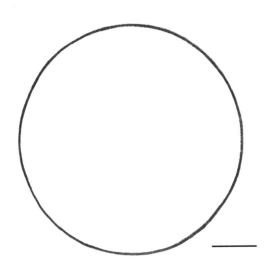 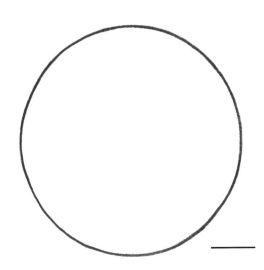

Time: _____   Time: _____

Orientation: Draw the icons you have learned in context. After your drawings are complete, express the meaning of each in sign language and then in spoken language.

6.7

6.8

6.6

6.5

6.0 BUSINESS PRACTICES

Tenet: Interpreters maintain ethical business practices.

Illustrative Behavior - Interpreters:

6.1 Accurately represent qualifications, such as certification, educational background, and experience, and provide documentation when requested.

6.2 Honor professional commitments and terminate assignments only when fair and justifiable grounds exist.

6.3 Promote conditions that are conducive to effective communication, inform the parties involved if such conditions do not exist, and seek appropriate remedies.

6.4 Inform appropriate parties in a timely manner when delayed or unable to fulfill assignments.

6.5 Reserve the option to decline or discontinue assignments if working conditions are not safe, healthy, or conducive to interpreting.

6.6 **Refrain from harassment or coercion before, during, or after the provision of interpreting services.**

6.7 Render pro bono services in a fair and reasonable manner.

6.8 Charge fair and reasonable fees for the performance of interpreting services and arrange for payment in a professional and judicious manner.

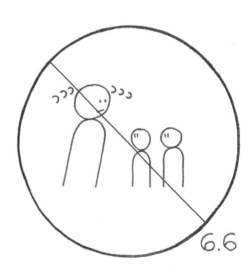

6.6

6.6 Refrain from harassment or coercion before, during, or after the provision of interpreting services.

Explanation:

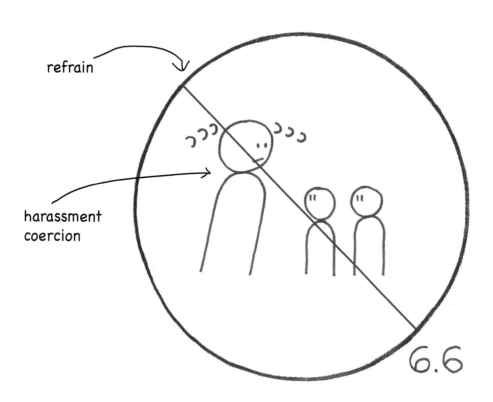

Imitation: Trace the image below.

6.6

Comprehension:

Expression: Draw with understanding.

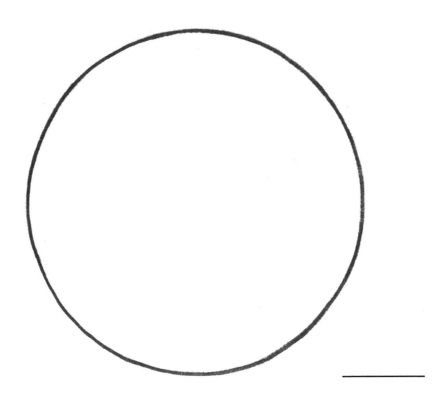

_____

Reflection: Make notes about the meaning.
Clarify your understanding or write down questions to address with a mentor.

_____

_____

_____

_____

_____

Memorization: Practice drawing without turning back to see the original.

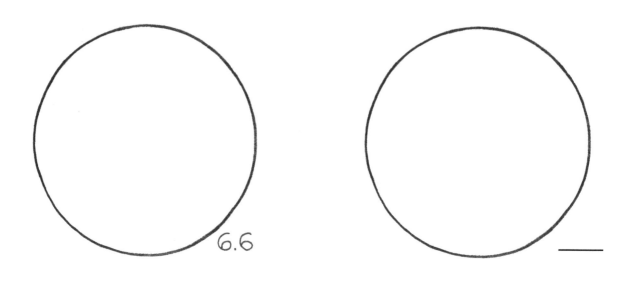

6.6

Check for accuracy. If you know it, save these others for future review.

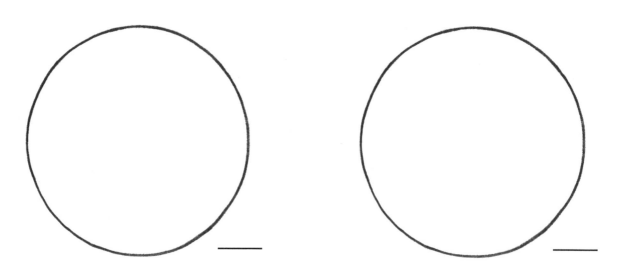

Acceleration: Practice drawing as quickly as possible.
Compare to original to ensure nothing was overlooked.

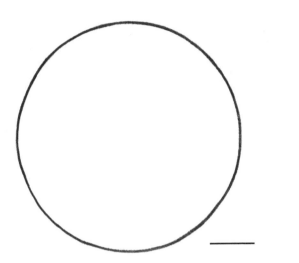 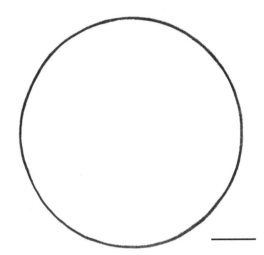

Time yourself. Be sure your drawing is complete within 15 seconds.
Jot down your time below. Be aware which drawings require more time.

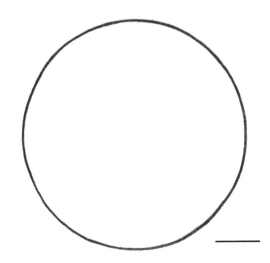 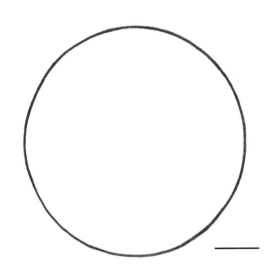

Time: _____   Time: _____

Orientation: Draw the icons you have learned in context. After your drawings are complete, express the meaning of each in sign language and then in spoken language.

6.7

6.8

6.0 BUSINESS PRACTICES

Tenet: Interpreters maintain ethical business practices.

Illustrative Behavior - Interpreters:

6.1 Accurately represent qualifications, such as certification, educational background, and experience, and provide documentation when requested.

6.2 Honor professional commitments and terminate assignments only when fair and justifiable grounds exist.

6.3 Promote conditions that are conducive to effective communication, inform the parties involved if such conditions do not exist, and seek appropriate remedies.

6.4 Inform appropriate parties in a timely manner when delayed or unable to fulfill assignments.

6.5 Reserve the option to decline or discontinue assignments if working conditions are not safe, healthy, or conducive to interpreting.

6.6 Refrain from harassment or coercion before, during, or after the provision of interpreting services.

6.7 Render pro bono services in a fair and reasonable manner.

6.8 Charge fair and reasonable fees for the performance of interpreting services and arrange for payment in a professional and judicious manner.

6.7

6.7 Render pro bono services in a fair and reasonable manner.

Explanation:

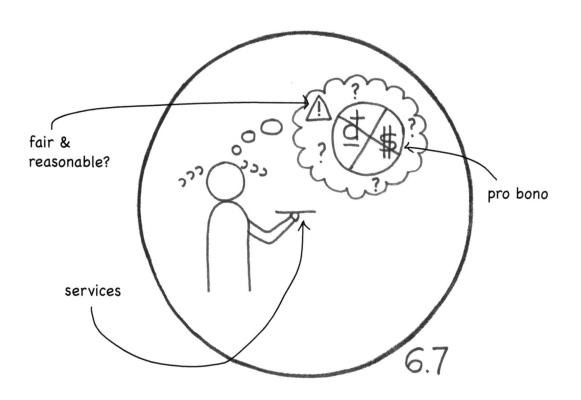

Imitation: Trace the image below.

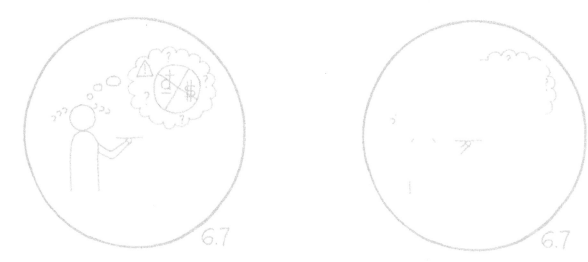

Comprehension:

Expression: Draw with understanding.

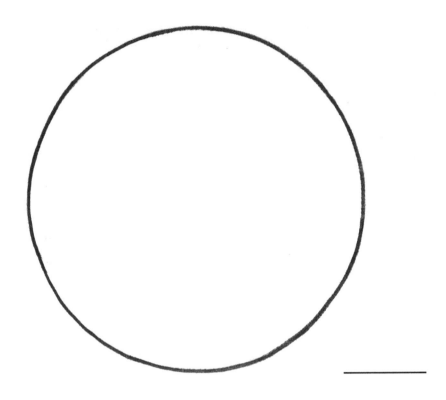

Reflection: Make notes about the meaning.
Clarify your understanding or write down questions to address with a mentor.

_____

_____

_____

_____

_____

Memorization: Practice drawing without turning back to see the original.

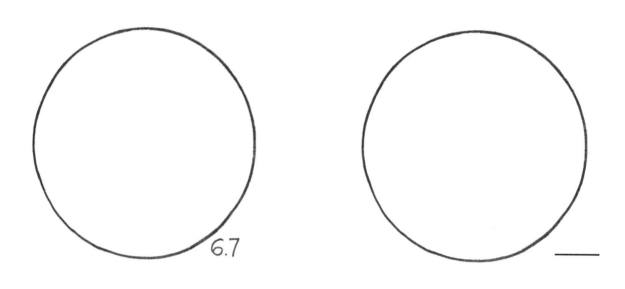

6.7

Check for accuracy. If you know it, save these others for future review.

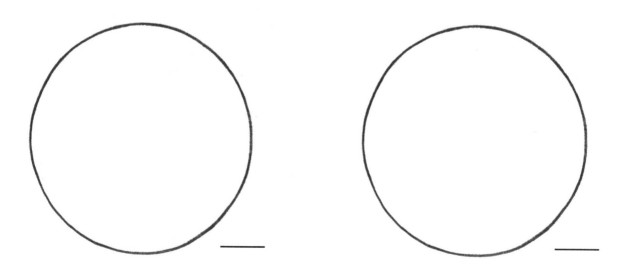

Acceleration: Practice drawing as quickly as possible.
Compare to original to ensure nothing was overlooked.

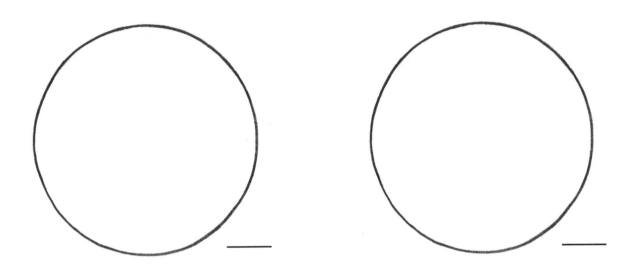

Time yourself. Be sure your drawing is complete within 15 seconds.
Jot down your time below. Be aware which drawings require more time.

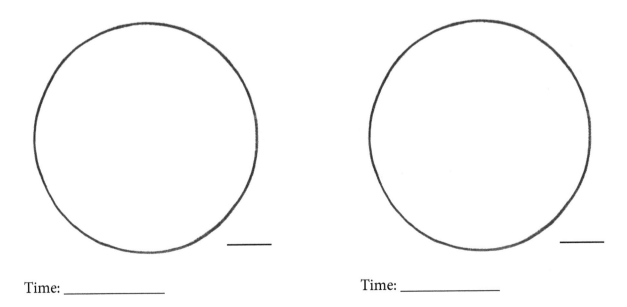

Time: _____

Time: _____

Orientation: Draw the icons you have learned in context. After your drawings are complete, express the meaning of each in sign language and then in spoken language.

6.8

6.0 BUSINESS PRACTICES

Tenet: Interpreters maintain ethical business practices.

Illustrative Behavior - Interpreters:

6.1 Accurately represent qualifications, such as certification, educational background, and experience, and provide documentation when requested.

6.2 Honor professional commitments and terminate assignments only when fair and justifiable grounds exist.

6.3 Promote conditions that are conducive to effective communication, inform the parties involved if such conditions do not exist, and seek appropriate remedies.

6.4 Inform appropriate parties in a timely manner when delayed or unable to fulfill assignments.

6.5 Reserve the option to decline or discontinue assignments if working conditions are not safe, healthy, or conducive to interpreting.

6.6 Refrain from harassment or coercion before, during, or after the provision of interpreting services.

6.7 Render pro bono services in a fair and reasonable manner.

6.8 Charge fair and reasonable fees for the performance of interpreting services and arrange for payment in a professional and judicious manner.

6.8

6.8 Charge fair and reasonable fees for the performance of interpreting services and arrange for payment in a professional and judicious manner.

Explanation:

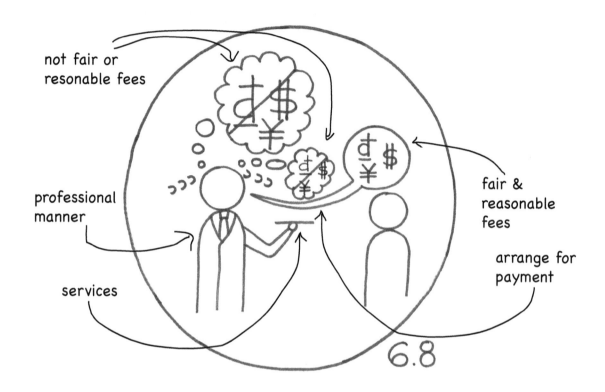

Imitation: Trace the image below.

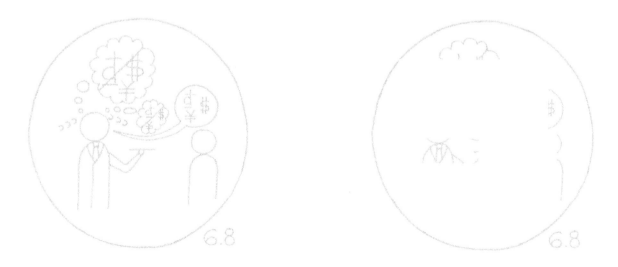

Comprehension:

Expression: Draw with understanding.

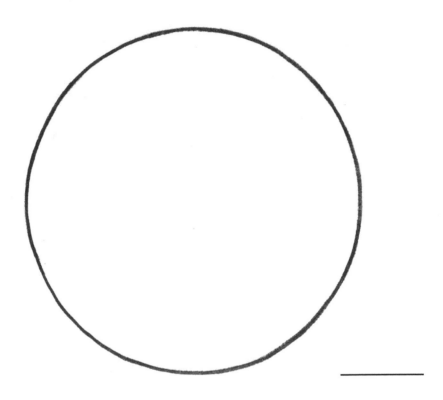

Reflection: Make notes about the meaning.
Clarify your understanding or write down questions to address with a mentor.

_____

_____

_____

_____

_____

Memorization: Practice drawing without turning back to see the original.

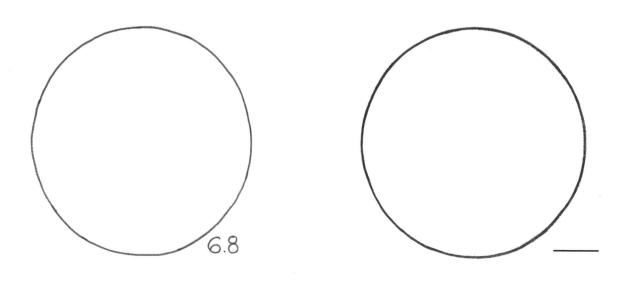

6.8

Check for accuracy. If you know it, save these others for future review.

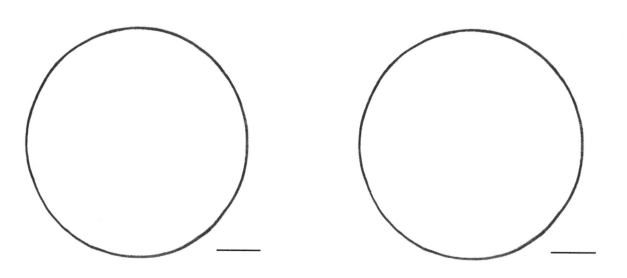

Acceleration: Practice drawing as quickly as possible.
Compare to original to ensure nothing was overlooked.

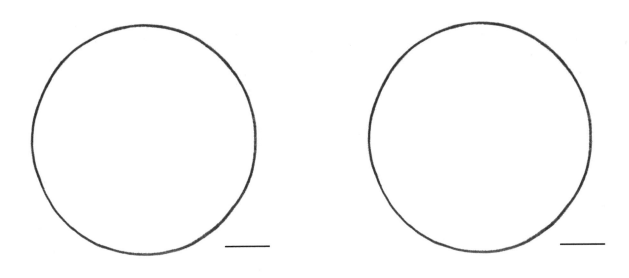

Time yourself. Be sure your drawing is complete within 15 seconds.
Jot down your time below. Be aware which drawings require more time.

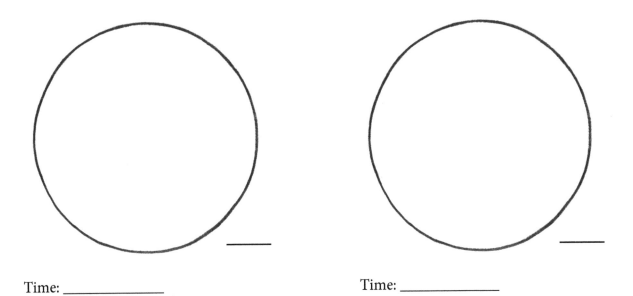

Time: _____

Time: _____

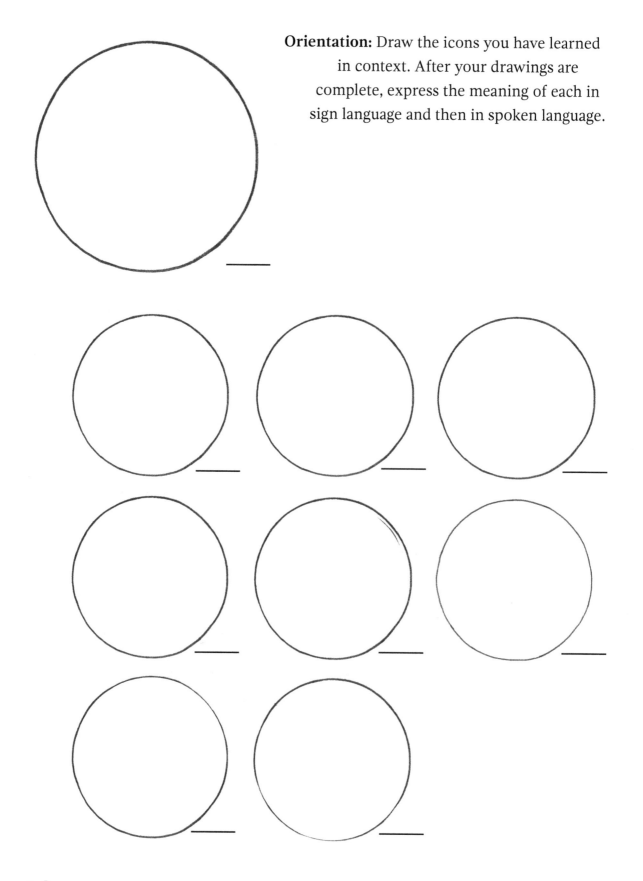

Orientation: Draw the icons you have learned in context. After your drawings are complete, express the meaning of each in sign language and then in spoken language.

6.8

7.0 PROFESSIONAL DEVELOPMENT

Tenet: Interpreters engage in professional development.

Illustrative Behavior - Interpreters:

7.1 Increase knowledge and strengthen skills through activities such as:
- pursuing higher education;
- attending workshops and conferences;
- seeking mentoring and supervision opportunities;
- participating in community events; and
- engaging in independent studies.

7.2 Keep abreast of laws, policies, rules, and regulations that affect the profession.

7.0

7.0 Tenet: Interpreters engage in professional development.

Explanation:

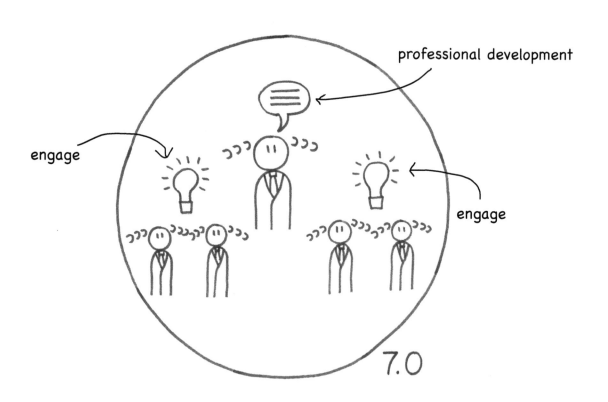

Imitation: Trace the image below.

Comprehension:

Expression: Draw with understanding.

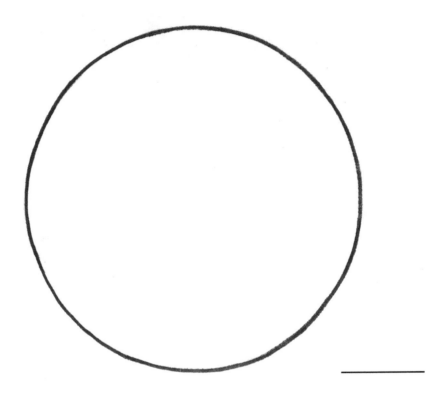

Reflection: Make notes about the meaning.

Clarify your understanding or write down questions to address with a mentor.

_____

_____

_____

_____

_____

Memorization: Practice drawing without turning back to see the original.

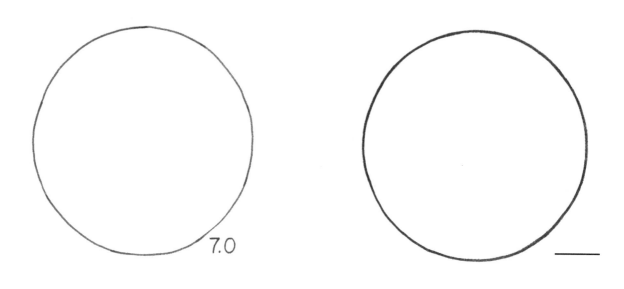

7.0

Check for accuracy. If you know it, save these others for future review.

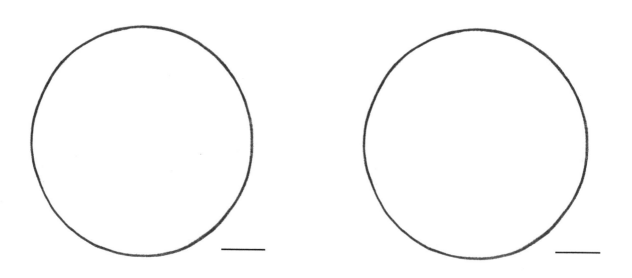

Acceleration: Practice drawing as quickly as possible.
Compare to original to ensure nothing was overlooked.

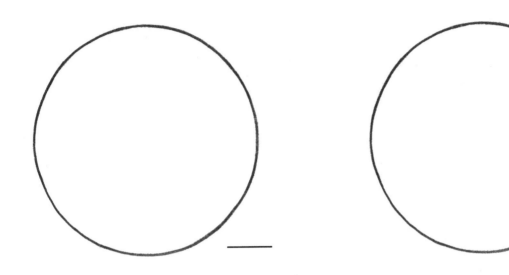

Time yourself. Be sure your drawing is complete within 15 seconds.
Jot down your time below. Be aware which drawings require more time.

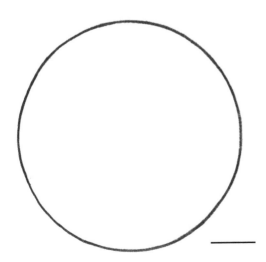

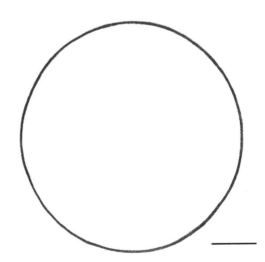

Time: _____

Time: _____

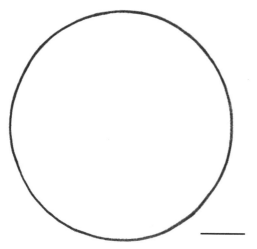

Orientation: Draw the icons you have learned in context. After your drawings are complete, express the meaning of each in sign language and then in spoken language.

7.1

7.2

7.0 PROFESSIONAL DEVELOPMENT

Tenet: Interpreters engage in professional development.

Illustrative Behavior - Interpreters:

7.1 **Increase knowledge and strengthen skills through activities such as:**
- **pursuing higher education;**
- **attending workshops and conferences;**
- **seeking mentoring and supervision opportunities;**
- **participating in community events; and**
- **engaging in independent studies.**

7.2 Keep abreast of laws, policies, rules, and regulations that affect the profession.

7.1

7.1 Increase knowledge and strengthen skills through various activities.

Explanation:

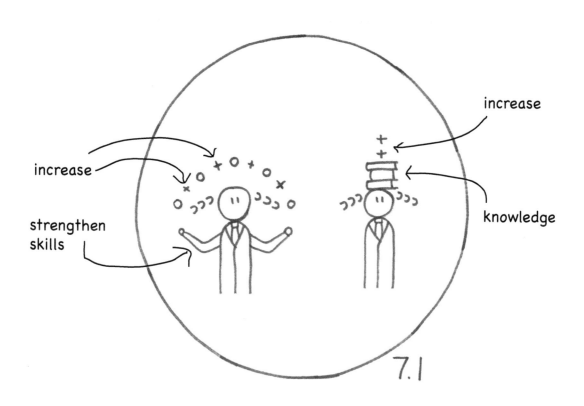

Imitation: Trace the image below.

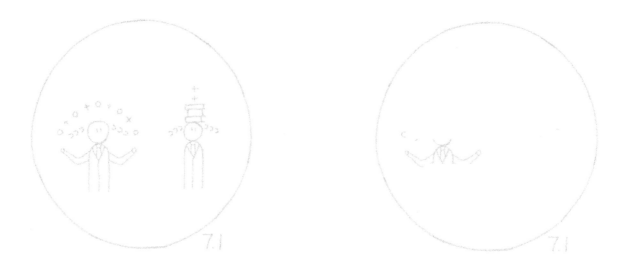

Comprehension:

Expression: Draw with understanding.

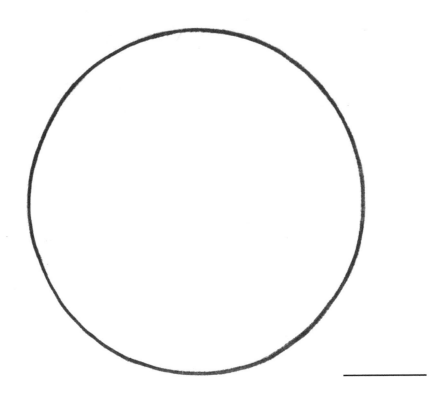

Reflection: Make notes about the meaning.
Clarify your understanding or write down questions to address with a mentor.

_____

_____

_____

_____

_____

Memorization: Practice drawing without turning back to see the original.

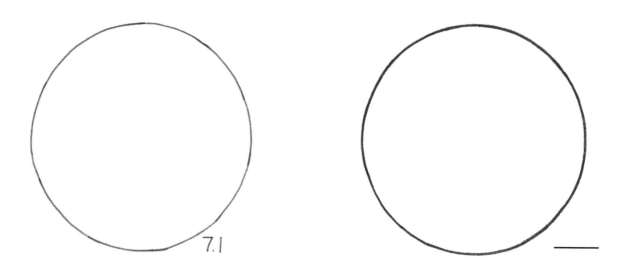

7.1

Check for accuracy. If you know it, save these others for future review.

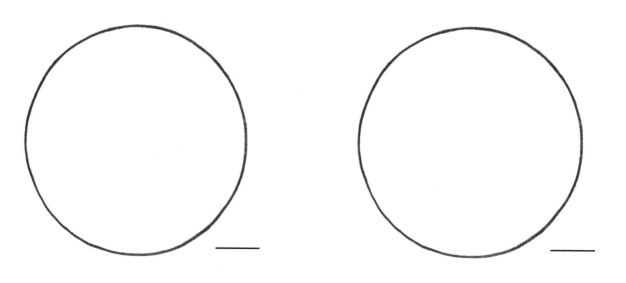

Acceleration: Practice drawing as quickly as possible.
Compare to original to ensure nothing was overlooked.

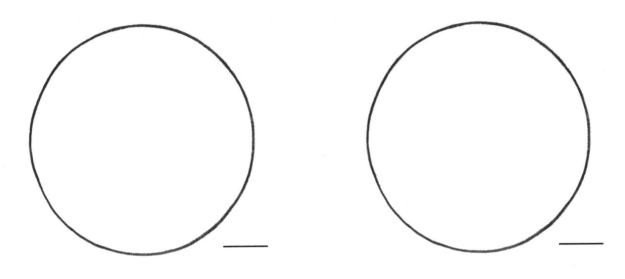

Time yourself. Be sure your drawing is complete within 15 seconds.
Jot down your time below. Be aware which drawings require more time.

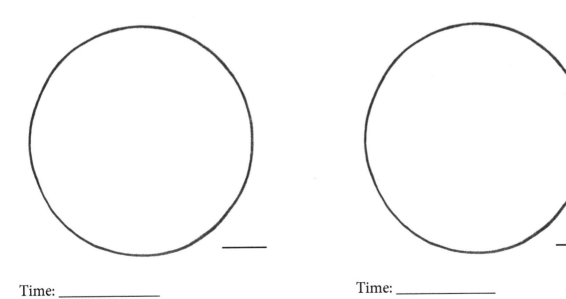

Time: _____   Time: _____

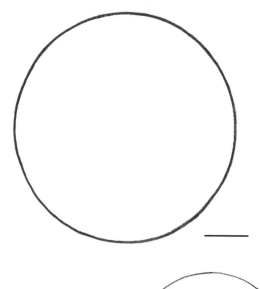

Orientation: Draw the icons you have learned in context. After your drawings are complete, express the meaning of each in sign language and then in spoken language.

_____

_____

7.2

7.0 PROFESSIONAL DEVELOPMENT

Tenet: Interpreters engage in professional development.

Illustrative Behavior - Interpreters:

7.1 Increase knowledge and strengthen skills through activities such as:
- pursuing higher education;
- attending workshops and conferences;
- seeking mentoring and supervision opportunities;
- participating in community events; and
- engaging in independent studies.

7.2 Keep abreast of laws, policies, rules, and regulations that affect the profession.

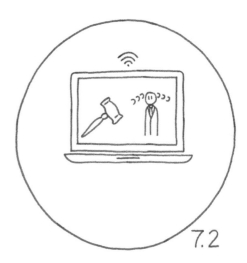

7.2

7.2 Keep abreast of laws, policies, rules, and regulations that affect the profession.

Explanation:

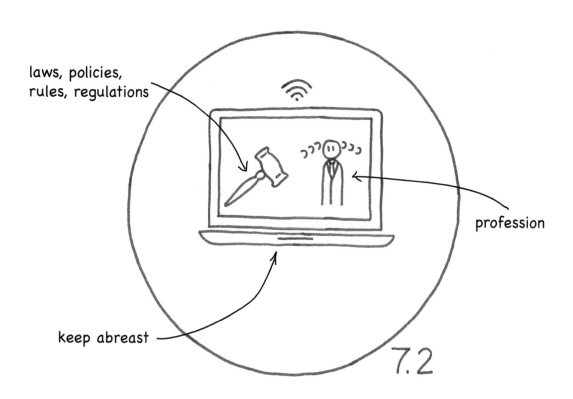

Imitation: Trace the image below.

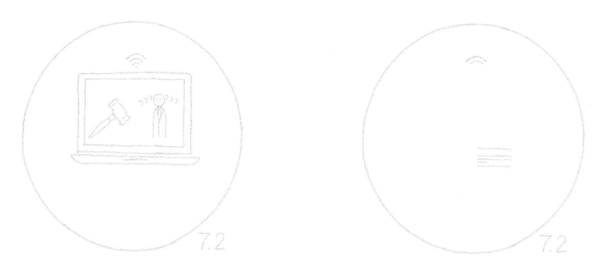

Comprehension:

Expression: Draw with understanding.

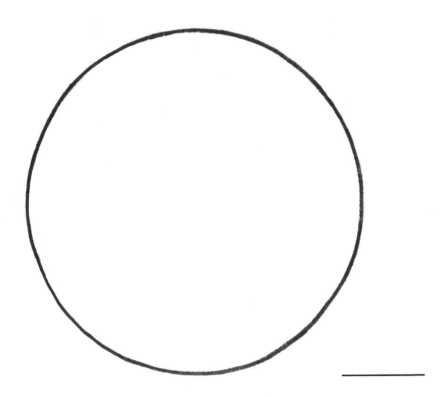

Reflection: Make notes about the meaning.
Clarify your understanding or write down questions to address with a mentor.

_____

_____

_____

_____

_____

7.2

Memorization: Practice drawing without turning back to see the original.

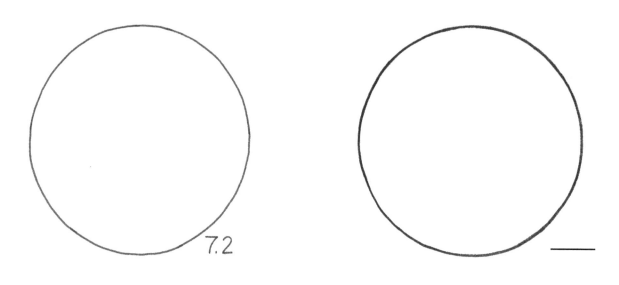

7.2

Check for accuracy. If you know it, save these others for future review.

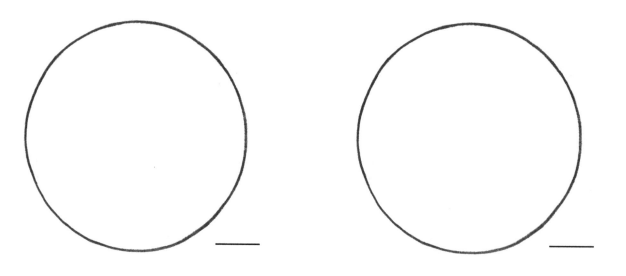

Acceleration: Practice drawing as quickly as possible.
Compare to original to ensure nothing was overlooked.

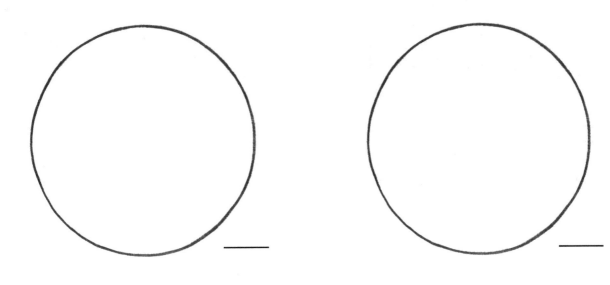

Time yourself. Be sure your drawing is complete within 15 seconds.
Jot down your time below. Be aware which drawings require more time.

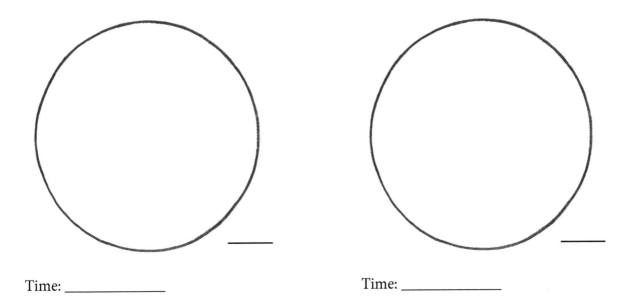

Time: _____

Time: _____

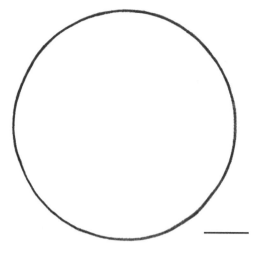

Orientation: Draw the icons you have learned in context. After your drawings are complete, express the meaning of each in sign language and then in spoken language.

_____

_____

_____

7.2

RID CODE OF PROFESSIONAL CONDUCT

1. Interpreters adhere to standards of confidential communication.
2. Interpreters possess the professional skills and knowledge required for the specific interpreting situation.
3. Interpreters conduct themselves in a manner appropriate to the specific interpreting situation.
4. Interpreters demonstrate respect for consumers.
5. Interpreters demonstrate respect for colleagues, interns, and students of the profession.
6. Interpreters maintain ethical business practices.
7. Interpreters engage in professional development.

APPLICABILITY

A. This Code of Professional Conduct applies to certified and associate members of the Registry of Interpreters for the Deaf, Inc., Certified members of the National Association of the Deaf, interns, and students of the profession.
B. Federal, state or other statutes or regulations may supersede this Code of Professional Conduct. When there is a conflict between this code and local, state, or federal laws and regulations, the interpreter obeys the rule of law.
C. This Code of Professional Conduct applies to interpreted situations that are performed either face-to-face or remotely.

DEFINITIONS

For the purpose of this document, the following terms are used:

- Colleagues: Other interpreters.
- Conflict of Interest: A conflict between the private interests (personal, financial, or professional) and the official or professional responsibilities of an interpreter in a position of trust, whether actual or perceived, deriving from a specific interpreting situation.
- Consumers: Individuals and entities who are part of the interpreted situation. This includes individuals who are deaf, deaf-blind, hard of hearing, and hearing.

1.0 CONFIDENTIALITY

Tenet: Interpreters adhere to standards of confidential communication.

Guiding Principle: Interpreters hold a position of trust in their role as linguistic and cultural facilitators of communication. Confidentiality is highly valued by consumers and is essential to protecting all involved.

Each interpreting situation (e.g., elementary, secondary, and post-secondary education, legal, medical, mental health) has a standard of confidentiality. Under the reasonable interpreter standard, professional interpreters are expected to know the general requirements and applicability of various levels of confidentiality. Exceptions to confidentiality include, for example, federal and state laws requiring mandatory reporting of abuse or threats of suicide, or responding to subpoenas.

Illustrative Behavior - Interpreters:

1.1 Share assignment-related information only on a confidential and "as-needed" basis (e.g., supervisors, interpreter team members, members of the educational team, hiring entities).

1.2 Manage data, invoices, records, or other situational or consumer-specific information in a manner consistent with maintaining consumer confidentiality (e.g., shredding, locked files).

1.3 Inform consumers when federal or state mandates require disclosure of confidential information.

2.0 PROFESSIONALISM

Tenet: Interpreters possess the professional skills and knowledge required for the specific interpreting situation.

Guiding Principle: Interpreters are expected to stay abreast of evolving language use and trends in the profession of interpreting as well as in the American Deaf community.

Interpreters accept assignments using discretion with regard to skill, communication mode, setting, and consumer needs. Interpreters possess knowledge of American Deaf culture and deafness-related resources.

Illustrative Behavior - Interpreters:

2.1 Provide service delivery regardless of race, color, national origin, gender, religion, age, disability, sexual orientation, or any other factor.

2.2 Assess consumer needs and the interpreting situation before and during the assignment and make adjustments as needed.

2.3 Render the message faithfully by conveying the content and spirit of what is being communicated, using language most readily understood by consumers, and correcting errors discreetly and expeditiously.

2.4 Request support (e.g., certified deaf interpreters, team members, language facilitators) when needed to fully convey the message or to address exceptional communication challenges (e.g. cognitive disabilities, foreign sign language, emerging language ability, or lack of formal instruction or language).

2.5 Refrain from providing counsel, advice, or personal opinions.

2.6 Judiciously provide information or referral regarding available interpreting or community resources without infringing upon consumers' rights.

Tenet: Interpreters conduct themselves in a manner appropriate to the specific interpreting situation.

Guiding Principle: Interpreters are expected to present themselves appropriately in demeanor and appearance. They avoid situations that result in conflicting roles or perceived or actual conflicts of interest.

Illustrative Behavior - Interpreters:

3.1 Consult with appropriate persons regarding the interpreting situation to determine issues such as placement and adaptations necessary to interpret effectively.

3.2 Decline assignments or withdraw from the interpreting profession when not competent due to physical, mental, or emotional factors.

3.3 Avoid performing dual or conflicting roles in interdisciplinary (e.g. educational or mental health teams) or other settings.

3.4 Comply with established workplace codes of conduct, notify appropriate personnel if there is a conflict with this Code of Professional Conduct, and actively seek resolution where warranted.

3.5 Conduct and present themselves in an unobtrusive manner and exercise care in choice of attire.

3.6 Refrain from the use of mind-altering substances before or during the performance of duties.

3.7 Disclose to parties involved any actual or perceived conflicts of interest.

3.8 Avoid actual or perceived conflicts of interest that might cause harm or interfere with the effectiveness of interpreting services.

3.9 Refrain from using confidential interpreted information for personal, monetary, or professional gain.

3.10 Refrain from using confidential interpreted information for the benefit of personal or professional affiliations or entities.

4.0 RESPECT FOR CONSUMERS

Tenet: Interpreters demonstrate respect for consumers.

Guiding Principle: Interpreters are expected to honor consumer preferences in selection of interpreters and interpreting dynamics, while recognizing the realities of qualifications, availability, and situation.

Illustrative Behavior - Interpreters:

4.1 Consider consumer requests or needs regarding language preferences, and render the message accordingly (interpreted or transliterated).

4.2 Approach consumers with a professional demeanor at all times.

4.3 Obtain the consent of consumers before bringing an intern to an assignment.

4.4 Facilitate communication access and equality, and support the full interaction and independence of consumers.

5.0 RESPECT FOR COLLEAGUES

Tenet: Interpreters demonstrate respect for colleagues, interns and students of the profession.

Guiding Principle: Interpreters are expected to collaborate with colleagues to foster the delivery of effective interpreting services. They also understand that the manner in which they relate to colleagues reflects upon the profession in general.

Illustrative Behavior - Interpreters:

5.1 Maintain civility toward colleagues, interns, and students.

5.2 Work cooperatively with team members through consultation before assignments regarding logistics, providing professional and courteous assistance when asked and monitoring the accuracy of the message while functioning in the role of the support interpreter.

5.3 Approach colleagues privately to discuss and resolve breaches of ethical or professional conduct through standard conflict resolution methods; file a formal grievance only after such attempts have been unsuccessful or the breaches are harmful or habitual.

5.4 Assist and encourage colleagues by sharing information and serving as mentors when appropriate.

5.5 Obtain the consent of colleagues before bringing an intern to an assignment.

6.0 BUSINESS PRACTICES

Tenet: Interpreters maintain ethical business practices.

Guiding Principle: Interpreters are expected to conduct their business in a professional manner whether in private practice or in the employ of an agency or other entity. Professional interpreters are entitled to a living wage based on their qualifications and expertise. Interpreters are also entitled to working conditions conducive to effective service delivery.

Illustrative Behavior - Interpreters:

6.1 Accurately represent qualifications, such as certification, educational background, and experience, and provide documentation when requested.

6.2 Honor professional commitments and terminate assignments only when fair and justifiable grounds exist.

6.3 Promote conditions that are conducive to effective communication, inform the parties involved if such conditions do not exist, and seek appropriate remedies.

6.4 Inform appropriate parties in a timely manner when delayed or unable to fulfill assignments.

6.5 Reserve the option to decline or discontinue assignments if working conditions are not safe, healthy, or conducive to interpreting.

6.6 Refrain from harassment or coercion before, during, or after the provision of interpreting services.

6.7 Render pro bono services in a fair and reasonable manner.

6.8 Charge fair and reasonable fees for the performance of interpreting services and arrange for payment in a professional and judicious manner.

7.0 PROFESSIONAL DEVELOPMENT

Tenet: Interpreters engage in professional development.

Guiding Principle: Interpreters are expected to foster and maintain interpreting competence and the stature of the profession through ongoing development of knowledge and skills.

Illustrative Behavior - Interpreters:

7.1 Increase knowledge and strengthen skills through activities such as:
- pursuing higher education;
- attending workshops and conferences;
- seeking mentoring and supervision opportunities;
- participating in community events; and
- engaging in independent studies.

7.2 Keep abreast of laws, policies, rules, and regulations that affect the profession.

CPC

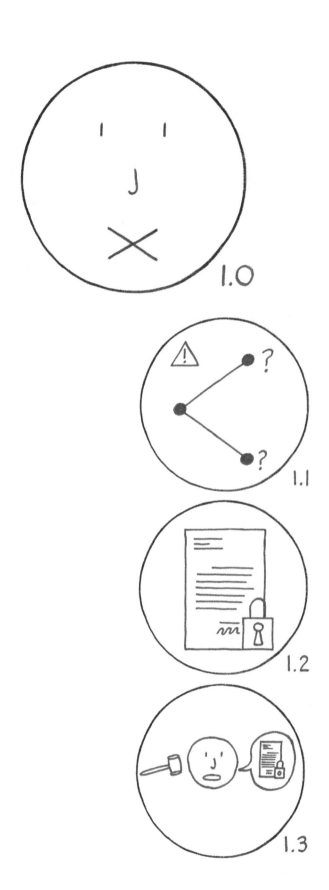

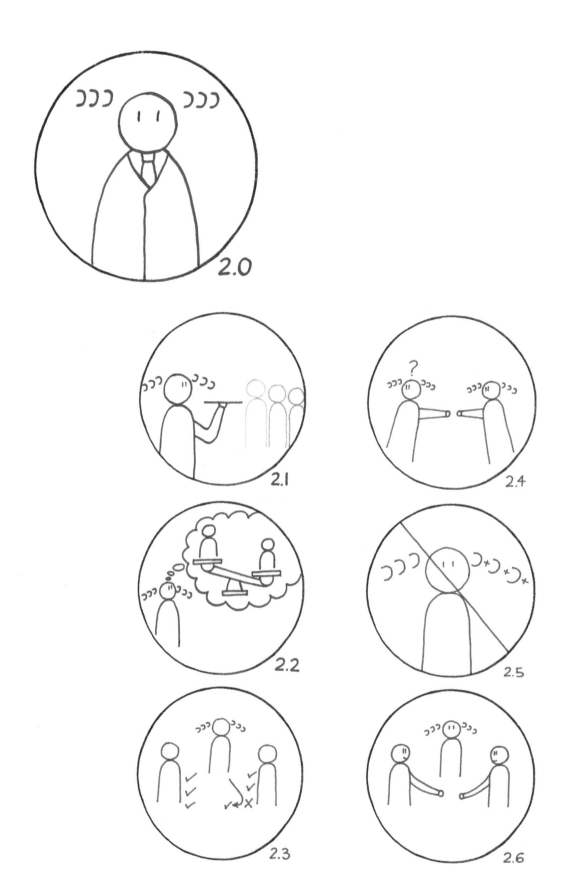

CPC VISUALLY

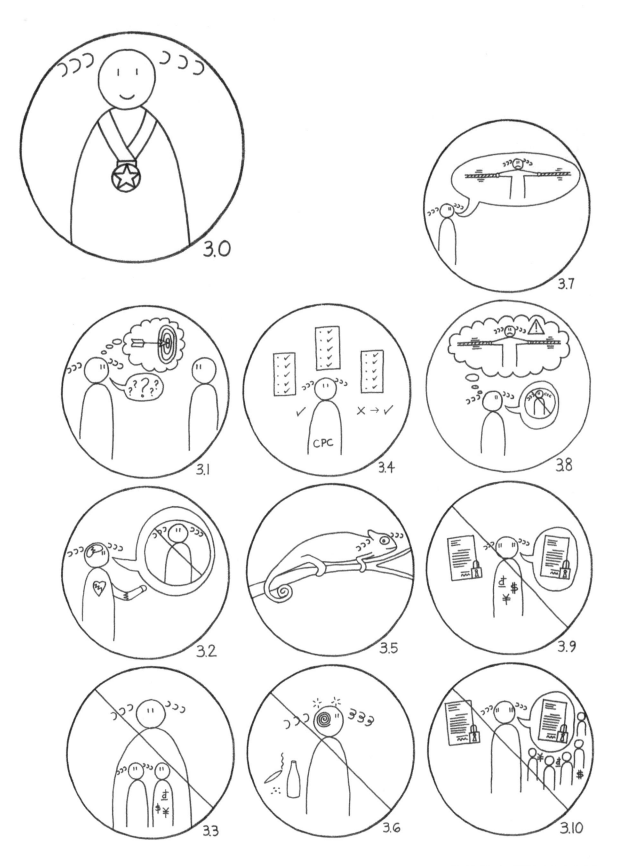

CPC VISUALLY

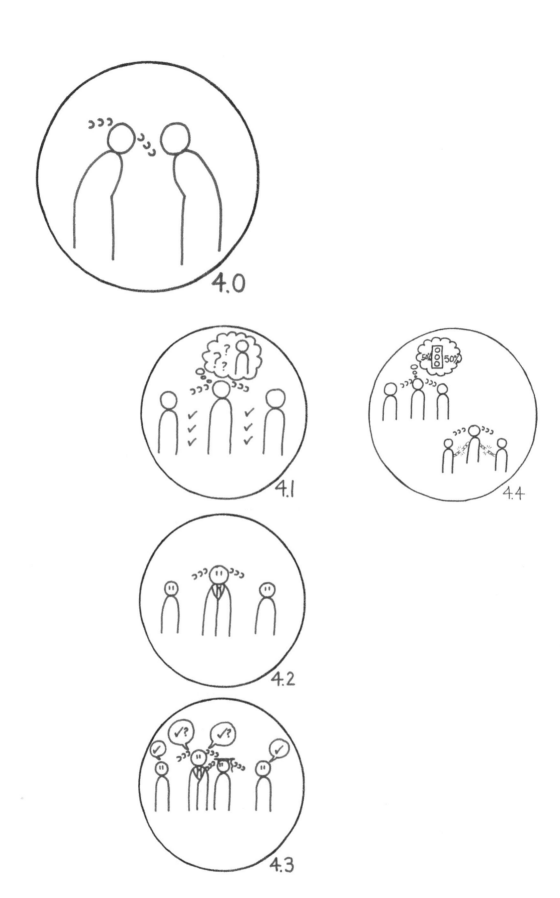

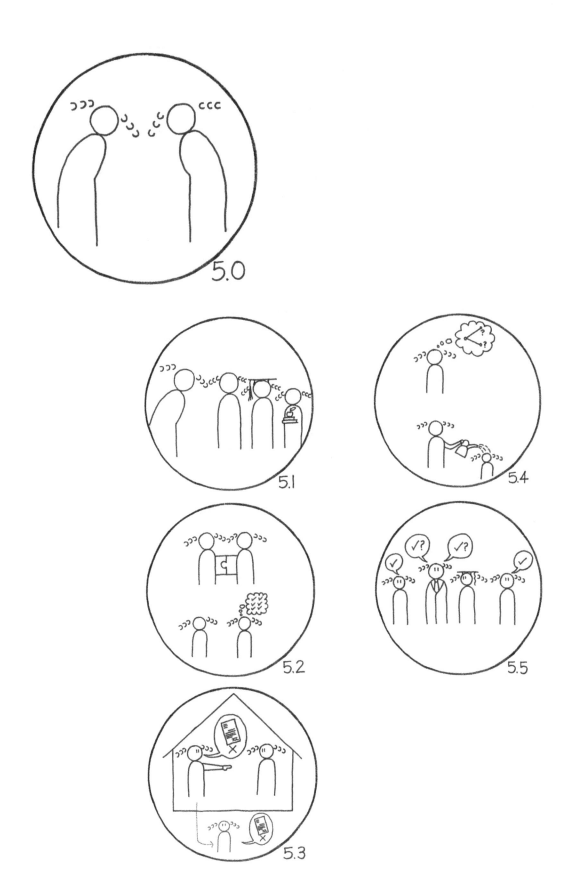

CPC VISUALLY

CPC VISUALLY

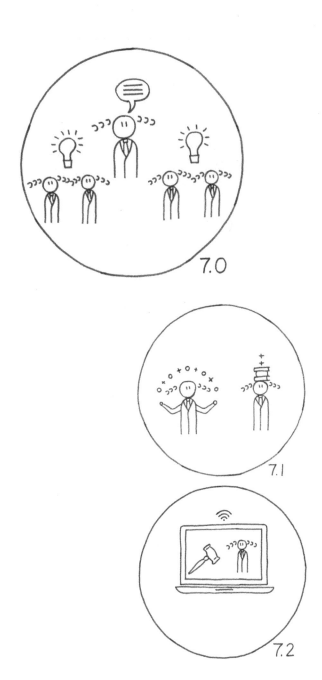

7.0

7.1

7.2

CPC VISUALLY PRACTICE SHEETS

Orientation: Draw the icons you have learned in context.

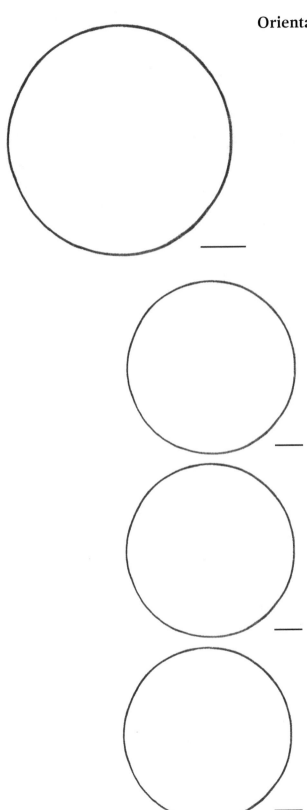

CPC VISUALLY PRACTICE SHEETS 1.0

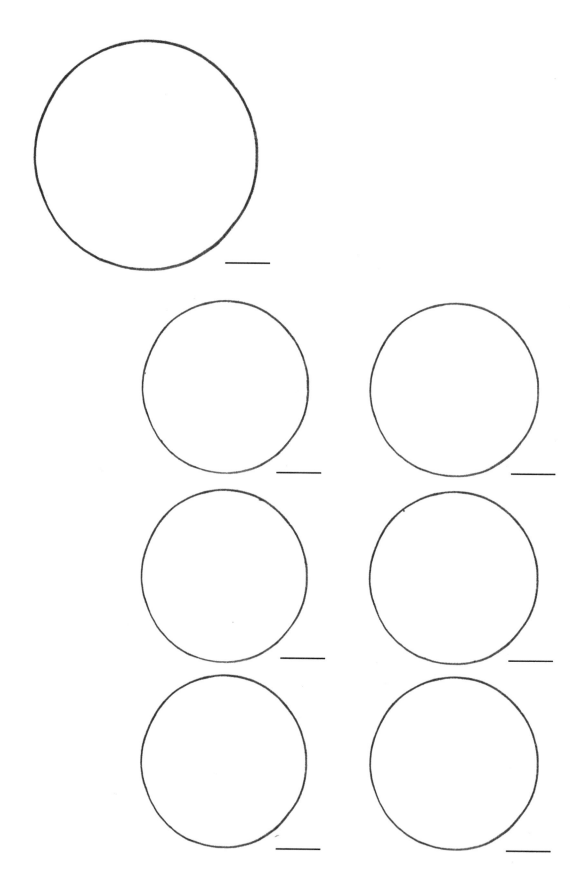

CPC VISUALLY PRACTICE SHEETS 2.0

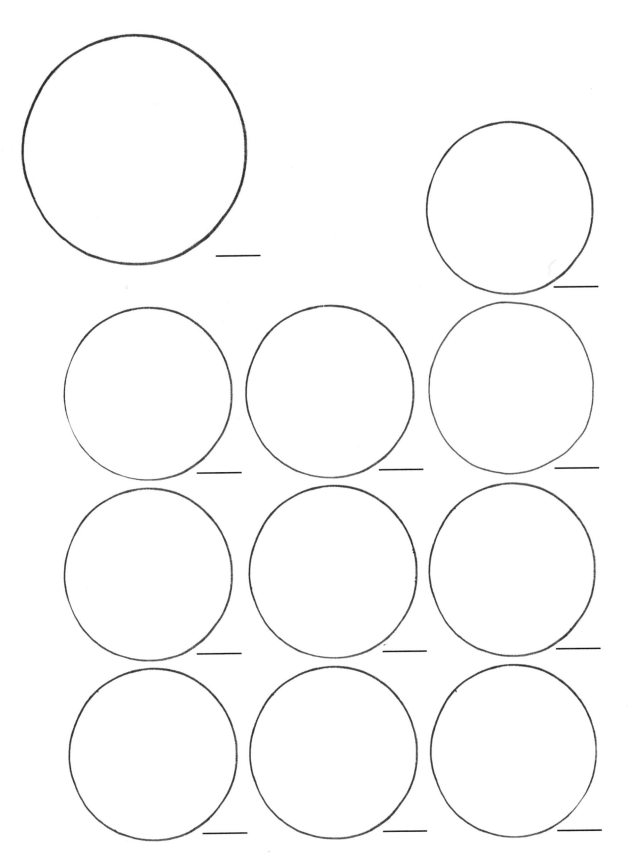

CPC VISUALLY PRACTICE SHEETS 3.0

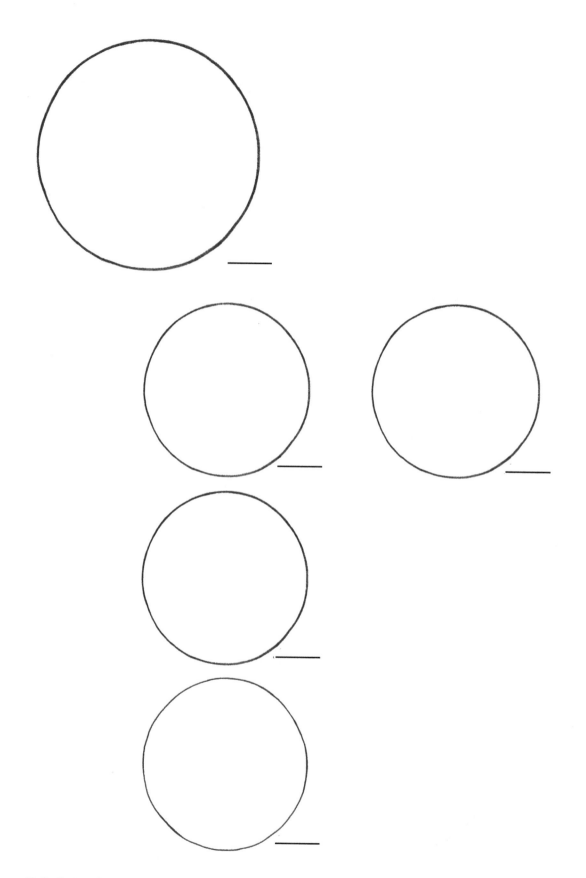

CPC VISUALLY PRACTICE SHEETS 4.0

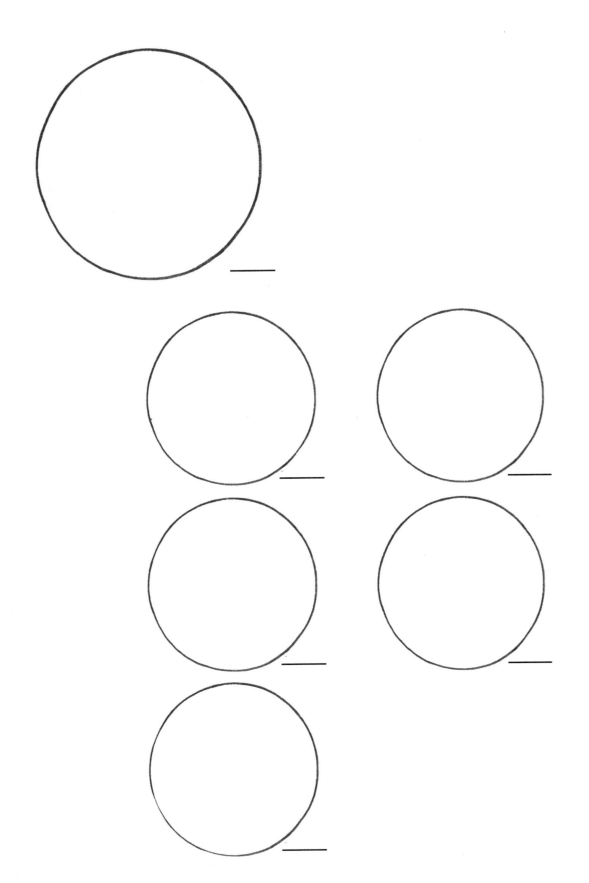

CPC VISUALLY PRACTICE SHEETS 5.0

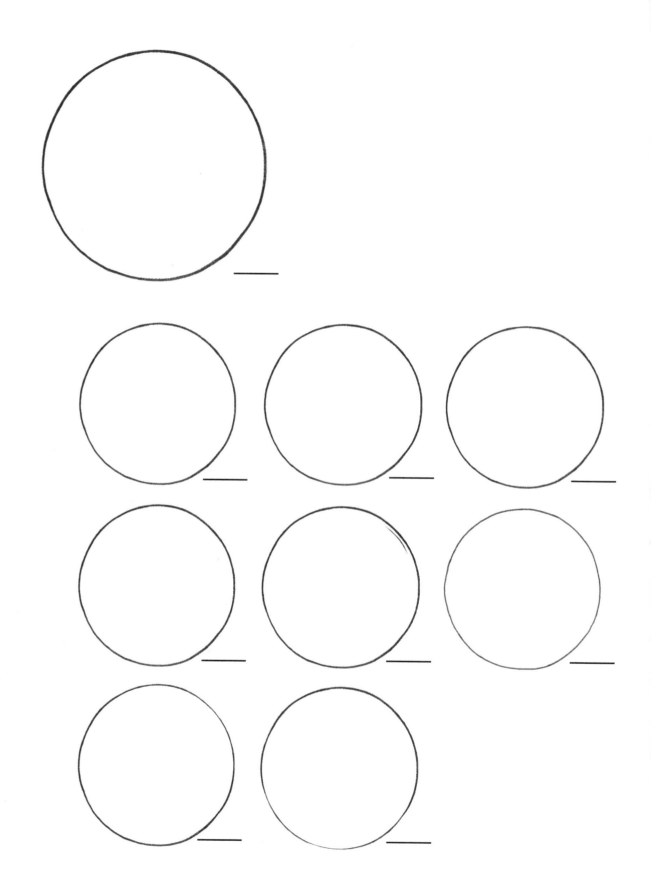

CPC VISUALLY PRACTICE SHEETS 6.0

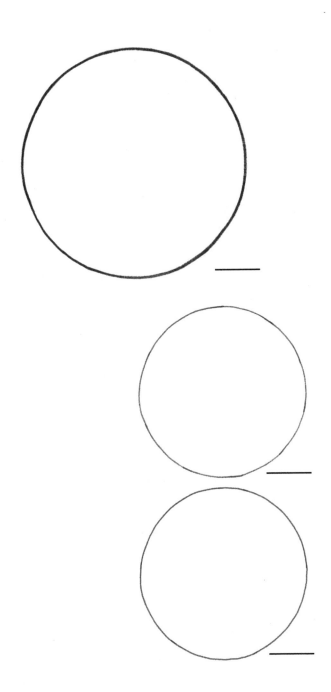

WHO IS DEAF DOORWAY?

Deaf Doorway seeks to open doors of opportunity for the Deaf around the world. The key themes for our work are:

- Accessibility – Deaf people need access to public information and services via sign language interpreting.
- Acquisition – Deaf people have a human right to acquire and develop proficiency in sign languages.
- Equal Participation – Deaf people need to have equal access to participation in personal, public and political arenas.

Our work is global. We go where we can be useful to the Deaf community to facilitate increasing access, understanding, and levels of engagement.

You can follow the activities of our work by signing up for our monthly newsletter at DeafDoorway.com. The proceeds from the sales of this book, in addition to all donations, are used to offset travel expenses and specific projects as listed on the website.

Our heart reaches out to the 35.5+ million culturally Deaf worldwide who need open doorways. Let's open the doorway together!

CPSIA information can be obtained
at www.ICGtesting.com
Printed in the USA
BVHW091532131221
623925BV00016B/679